RICS NEW RULES OF MEASUREMENT

Order of cost estimating and elemental cost planning

1st edition

Acknowledgments

The project stages from the *RIBA Outline Plan of Work 2007*, copyright Royal Institute of British Architects, are reproduced here with the permission of the RIBA.

Published by the Royal Institution of Chartered Surveyors (RICS)

Surveyor Court

Westwood Business Park

Coventry CV4 8JE

UK

www.ricsbooks.com

ISBN 978 1 84219 446 1

Typeset by Columns Design Ltd, Reading, Berks

Printed by Page Bros, Norwich

Contents

Foreword

Since 1922 the Standard Method of Measurement (SMM) has provided quantity surveyors with rules of measurement for building works. However, these rules were specifically drafted to advise quantity surveyors on how to measure building work items for inclusion in bills of quantities which, in turn, are used for the purpose of obtaining a tender price for a building project. Previous SMMs did not provide specific guidance on the measurement of building works for the purpose of producing cost estimates or *cost plans*. In the absence of any rules for measuring and describing building works for estimates and *cost plans*, quantity surveyors have generally adopted the principles described in the SMM. This, however, has resulted in inconsistent approaches being used by quantity surveyors to the measurement and description of building works for estimates and *cost plans*. This lack of consistency in measurement and description makes it extremely difficult for the *employer* and *project team* to understand what is included in the cost estimate, *cost limit* or *cost target* advised by the quantity surveyor; often resulting in doubts about the cost advice provided. Moreover, this lack of uniformity afforded a just ground of complaint on the part of the *employer*, as the *employer* was often left in doubt as to what was really included in a cost estimate or *cost plan*.

A Steering Group was set up by the RICS Quantity Surveying and Construction Professional Group to research the problems associated with the measurement of *building works* at all stages of the design and construction process. The Steering Group recognised that both the *employer* and the *project/design team* members need to have confidence in the measurement and cost information provided by the quantity surveyor; and quickly came to the conclusion that it was essential that guidance be made available to quantity surveyors so that a common and consistent basis is used to measure areas and *building works* items for the purpose of *order of cost estimates* and *cost plans*; as well as giving guidance on providing a structured approach for dealing with the other constituents needed to calculate cost estimates, *cost limits* or *cost targets*. Hence, it was decided that a bespoke set of measurement rules were required for the preparation of *order of cost estimates* and *elemental cost plans*.

Acknowledgments

The development of the *RICS new rules of measurement: Order of cost estimating and elemental cost planning* was facilitated by the RICS Quantity Surveying and Construction Professional Group under the direction of the Steering Group.

The members of the Steering Group formed to oversee drafting were:

- **Mr Ed Badke**: RICS Director for Construction and Built Environment
- **Mr David Benge**: Gleeds
- **Mr Michael Byng**: Chair of the RICS Quantity Surveying and Construction Professional Group
- **Mr Alan Cripps**: RICS
- **Mr John Davidson**: Consultant
- **Mr Stuart Earl**: Gleeds (Steering Group chair)
- **Mr John Kelly**: Axoss Ltd
- **Mr Joe Martin**: BCIS
- **Professor Gerry O'Sullivan**: RICS
- **Ms Leila Picken**: RICS
- **Mr Michael Rainbird**: Standing Joint Committee for the Standard Method of Measurement
- **Mr Tim Robinson**: RICS

The substantive drafting of the *RICS new rules of measurement: Order of cost estimating and elemental cost planning* was undertaken by Mr David Benge of Gleeds (95 New Cavendish Street, London WIW 6AF), *david.benge@gleeds.co.uk*

The Steering Group expresses its thanks to the professional and trade bodies, and to the quantity surveyors and building contractors, for their co-operation and advice in the detailed consultations that have taken place. The Steering Group also expresses its thanks to the surveyors who have assisted in testing the *RICS new rules of measurement: Order of cost estimating and elemental cost planning* and to the editors who have had the task of bringing together the final document.

Introduction

Status of the *RICS new rules of measurement*

These measurement rules have the same status as RICS guidance notes. The rules provide advice to RICS members on aspects of the profession. Where procedures are recommended for specific professional tasks, these are intended to embody 'best practice', i.e. procedures which in the opinion of RICS meet a high standard of professional competence.

Members are not required to follow the advice and recommendations contained in these rules. They should, however, note the following points.

When an allegation of professional negligence is made against a surveyor, the court is likely to take account of the contents of any relevant guidance notes published by RICS in deciding whether or not the surveyor had acted with reasonable competence.

In the opinion of RICS, a member conforming to the practices recommended in these rules should have at least a partial defence to an allegation of negligence by virtue of having followed these practices. However, members have the responsibility of deciding when it is inappropriate to follow the guidance.

On the other hand, it does not follow that members will be adjudged negligent if they have not followed the practices recommended in these rules. It is for each individual surveyor to decide on the appropriate procedure to follow in any professional task. However, where members depart from the practice recommended in these rules, they should do so only for a good reason. In the event of litigation, the court may require them to explain why they decided not to adopt the recommended practice. Also, if they have not followed this guidance, and their actions are called into question in an RICS disciplinary case, they will be asked to justify the steps they did take and this may be taken into account.

In addition, guidance notes (and equivalent materials) are relevant to professional competence in that each surveyor should be up to date and should have informed him or herself of guidance notes within a reasonable time of their promulgation.

Purpose of the document

The *RICS new rules of measurement* have been written to provide a standard set of measurement rules that are understandable by all those involved in a construction project, including the *employer*; thereby aiding communication between the *project/design team* and the *employer*. In addition, the *RICS new rules of measurement* should assist the quantity surveyor/cost manager in providing effective and accurate cost advice to the *employer* and the *project/design team*.

The document provides rules of measurement for the preparation of *order of cost estimates* and *elemental cost plans*. Direction on how to describe and deal with costs and allowances forming part of the cost of a building, but which are not reflected in the measurable *building work* items, is also provided.

The *RICS new rules of measurement* do not explain estimating methods, cost planning techniques, procurement methods or contract strategies; advice on these is obtainable in other RICS publications and from other external publications.

The *RICS new rules of measurement* are based on UK practice but the requirements for a coordinated set of rules and underlying philosophy behind each section have worldwide application.

Structure of the document

This document is divided into four parts with supporting appendices:

- **Part 1** places cost estimating and *elemental cost planning* in context with the *RIBA Plan of Work* and the *OGC Gateway Process*; and explains the symbols, abbreviations and definitions used in the rules.

- **Part 2** describes the purpose and content of an *order of cost estimate*; defines its key constituents, explains how to prepare an *order of cost estimate*; and sets out the rules of measurement for the preparation of *order of cost estimates* using the floor area method, *functional unit method* and *elemental method*.

- **Part 3** describes the purpose of *elemental cost plans*; explains their key constituents; and explains how to prepare an *elemental cost plan*.

- **Part 4** comprises the tabulated rules of measurement for the preparation of formal *elemental cost plans*.

- Appendices:

  - Appendix A: Core definition of gross internal area (GIA)

  - Appendix B: Commonly used functional units and functional units of measurement

  - Appendix C: Core definition of net internal area (NIA)

  - Appendix D: Special use definitions for shops

  - Appendix E: Measurement rules for elemental method of estimating

  - Appendix F: Logic and arrangement of levels 1 to 3 for elemental cost planning

  - Appendix G: Information requirements for formal cost plans

  - Appendix H: Template for elemental cost plan (based on level 1 codes)

  - Appendix I: Template for elemental cost plan (based on level 2 codes)

Use of the document

The *RICS new rules of measurement: Order of cost estimating and elemental cost planning* provide a structured basis for measuring *building work* and present a consistent approach for dealing with other key cost components associated with a building project when preparing *order of cost estimates* and *elemental cost plans*. The rules represent the essentials of good practice.

Users of the rules are advised to adopt metric units as the standard system of measurement. Where the *employer* requires reference to imperial units these may be provided as supplementary information (e.g. in parenthesis).

The British Standard BS 8888: 2006 *Technical Product Specification* (for defining, specifying and graphically representing products) recommends the inclusion of a comma rather than a point as a decimal marker, and a space instead of a comma as a thousand separator. Notwithstanding this, the traditional UK convention has been adopted in these rules (i.e. a point as a decimal marker and a comma as a thousand separator). Users should take care to ensure that this does not conflict with *employer* requirements.

Identity

The rules are called the *RICS new rules of measurement: Order of cost estimating and elemental cost planning*.

Enquiries

Enquiries concerning the rules may be made in the first instance to:

> Professional Information Department
>
> The Royal Institution of Chartered Surveyors (RICS)
>
> 12 Great George Street
>
> Parliament Square
>
> London SW1P 3AD
>
> United Kingdom

Any suggestions for future revisions are welcomed and may be sent to the Quantity Surveying and Construction Professional Group at RICS.

Part 1: General

Part 1: General

1.1 Introduction

1.1.1 This part places *order of cost estimating* and *elemental cost planning* in context with the *RIBA Plan of Work* and *OGC Gateway Process* and explains the symbols, abbreviations and definitions used in the rules.

1.2 Order of cost estimating and elemental cost planning in context with the RIBA Plan of Work and OGC Gateway Process

1.2.1 Throughout this document, references are made to both the *RIBA Plan of Work* and the *OGC Gateway Process* and the *RIBA Work Stages/OGC Gateways* within.

1.2.2 The *RIBA Plan of Work* is a construction industry recognised framework that organises the process of managing and designing building projects and administering building contracts into a number of key Work Stages. The *RIBA Plan of Work* has 11 sequential steps. Despite its apparent linear nature, it should be recognised that the sequence or content of *RIBA Work Stages* may need to be varied or overlapped to suit the proposed procurement method. Consequently, when two or more Work Stages are combined, it is not always transparent when a building project is moving from one stage to another. As such, it is an ideal tool, provided that it is conceptualised as providing the basic outline of the building project process.

1.2.3 As an alternative to the *RIBA Plan of Work*, central civil government, the health sector, local government and the defence sector have adopted the *OGC Gateway Process* as best practice for managing and designing building projects. The process examines programmes and projects at key decision points in their life cycle. It looks ahead to provide assurance that the *employer* can progress to the next stage. Project reviews are carried out under *OGC Gateway* Reviews 1 to 5. Typically a project will undergo three reviews before commitment to invest, and two looking at service implementation and confirmation of the operational benefits.

1.2.4 Both models are recognised frameworks for managing and designing building projects.

1.2.5 Cost estimates and *cost plans* will need to be prepared by the quantity surveyor/cost manager at various stages of the *RIBA Plan of Work* or at various gateways in the *OGC Gateway Process*, whichever management process is applicable. To address this requirement RICS has determined a series of formal cost estimating and *elemental cost planning* stages. These formal stages are shown in Figure 1 in the context of the *RIBA Work Stages* and *OGC Gateways*. Notwithstanding this, some *employers* may require the preparation of *cost plans* at different *RIBA Work Stages*. For example, some *employers* may ask for Formal Cost Plan 1 to be prepared at *Work Stage* C+ (*Work Stage* C+ being an *employer*-defined work stage, which occurs at a point between the completion of *Work Stage* C: Concept and *Work Stage* D: Design Development). *Work Stage* C+ would normally comprise the deliverables that the *employer* requires prior to submitting a building project for planning approval. It is essential, therefore, that the quantity surveyor/cost manager ascertains from the *employer* if there is to be any deviation from the recommended formal *cost planning* stages before commencing the *cost planning* process.

RIBA Work Stages		RICS formal cost estimating and elemental cost planning stages	OGC Gateways (Applicable to building projects)	
Preparation	A Appraisal	Order of cost estimate		
	B Design Brief		1 Business Justification	
	C Concept	Formal Cost Plan 1	2 Delivery Strategy	
			3A Design Brief and Concept Approval (See note below)	
Design	D Design Development	Formal Cost Plan 2		
	E Technical Design	Formal Cost Plan 3 Pre-tender estimate	3B Detailed Design Approval (See note below)	
Pre-Construction	F Production Information			
	G Tender Documentation			
	H Tender Action	Post tender estimate		
Construction	J Mobilisation		3C Investment Decision (See note below)	
	K Construction to Practical Completion		4 Readiness for Service	
Use	L Post Practical Completion		5 Operations Review and Benefits Realisation	

Note: A prerequisite of *OGC Gateway* Review 3: Investment Decision, is that the design brief, concept design and detailed design have been approved and signed off by the Senior Responsible Owner (SRO). For the purpose of comparing the *OGC Gateway Process* with the *RIBA Work Stages*, these two decision points are referred to as *OGC Gateway* 3A (Design Brief and Concept Approval) and *OGC Gateway* 3B (Detailed Design Approval); with *OGC Gateway* 3C representing the final *OGC Gateway* Review 3 (Investment Decision).

Figure 1: The RICS formal cost estimating and cost planning stages in context with the RIBA Plan of Work and OGC Gateways (adapted from the RIBA Outline Plan of Work 2007).

The project stages from the *RIBA Outline Plan of Work 2007*, copyright Royal Institute of British Architects, are reproduced here with the permission of the RIBA.

1.3   Symbols, abbreviations and definitions

Symbols, abbreviations and certain key words and phrases used in the rules are as detailed below.

1.3.1   Symbols used for measurement

ft²	square foot
ha	hectare
kg	kilogramme
kN	kilonewton
kW	kilowatt
m	linear metre
m²	square metre

m³	cubic metre
mm	millimetre
nr	number
t	tonne

1.3.2 Abbreviations

Cost/ft² of GIFA	cost per square foot of *gross internal floor area*
Cost/m² of GIFA	cost per square metre of *gross internal floor area*
EUQ	*element unit quantity*
EUR	*element unit rate*
GEA	*gross external floor area*
GIFA (GIA)	*gross internal floor area* (*gross internal area*)
NIA	*net internal area* (*net internal floor area*)
OCE	*order of cost estimates*
OGC	Office of Government Commerce
PC Sum	*prime cost sum*
RIBA	Royal Institute of British Architects
RICS	Royal Institution of Chartered Surveyors
RPI	retail price index (or indices)
SA	*site area*
TPI	tender price index (or indices)

1.3.3 Definitions

Authorised budget (or **approved estimate**) – See the definition for *cost limit*.

Base cost estimate – means an evolving estimate of known factors without any allowances for risk and uncertainty, or element of *inflation*. The *base cost estimate* is the sum of the *works cost estimate*, the *project/design team fees estimate* and the *other development/project costs* estimate.

Base date of cost data – means the date at which rates and prices contained within cost analyses or benchmark analyses are based.

Building work (or **building works**) – means all *components* measured and incorporated in *group elements* 1 to 9 (i.e. Substructure; Superstructure; Internal finishes; Fittings, furnishings and equipment; Services; Complete buildings and building units; Work to existing buildings; External works; and Facilitating works).

Building works estimate – means the sum of the cost targets for *group elements* 1 to 9 (i.e. Substructure; Superstructure; Internal finishes; Fittings, furnishings and equipment; Services; Complete buildings and building units; Work to existing buildings; External works; and Facilitating works). It excludes *main contractor's preliminaries* and *main contractor's overheads and profit*.

Component – means a measured item which forms part of an *element* or a *sub-element*. The quantity of one or more items will be measured and the cost estimated to ascertain the *cost target* for an *element* or a *sub-element*.

Construction inflation – means an allowance included in the *order of cost estimate* (OCE) or *cost plan* for fluctuations in the basic prices of labour, plant and equipment, and materials during the period from the date of tender return to the mid-point of the construction period. See also the definition for *tender inflation*.

Cost checks (**cost check** or **cost checking**) – take place during all design stages and are concerned with comparing current estimated costs against *cost targets* previously set for *elements* or *sub-elements* of the building.

Cost control – means the process of planning and controlling the costs of building(s). Takes place throughout complete duration of the construction project.

Cost limit (or **authorised budget** or **approved estimate**) – means the maximum expenditure that the *employer* is prepared to make in relation to the completed building.

Cost per functional unit (or **functional unit cost**) – is the *unit rate* which, when multiplied by the number of *functional units*, gives the total *building works estimate* (i.e. *works cost estimate* less *main contractor's preliminaries* and *main contractor's overheads and profit*). The total recommended *cost limit* (i.e. cost limit, including inflation) can also be expressed as a *cost per functional unit* when reporting costs.

Cost per m² of gross internal floor area (or **cost/m² of GIFA**) – is the *unit rate* which, when multiplied by the gross internal floor area (GIFA), gives the total *building works estimate* (i.e. *works cost estimate* less *main contractor's preliminaries* and *main contractor's overheads and profit*). Other cost estimates which form part of an *order of cost estimate* or a *cost plan* should also be converted to *costs/m² of GIFA* when reporting costs to the *employer* and *project team* (i.e. to express *cost targets* for *group elements*, *elements*, *sub-elements*, as well as the *cost limit*). They are also used in cost analyses and benchmarking as a means of documenting costs of previously completed building projects.

Cost plan – See the definition for *elemental cost plan*.

Cost target – means the recommended total expenditure for an *element*. The *cost target* for each *element* is likely to be derived from a number of *sub-elements* and *components*.

Design team – means architects, engineers and technology specialists responsible for the conceptual design aspects and their development into drawings, specifications and instructions required for construction of the building or facility and associated processes. The *design team* is a part of the *project team*.

Element – means a major part of a *group element* (e.g. the *elements* that create *group element* 1: Substructure are Foundations, Basement excavation, Basement retaining walls and Ground floor construction). A separate *cost target* can be established for each *element*.

Element unit quantity (EUQ) – is a unit of measurement which relates solely to the quantity of the *element* or *sub-element* itself (e.g. the area of the external walls, the area of windows and external doors and the number of internal doors).

Element unit rate (EUR) – means the total cost of an *element* divided by the *element unit quantity* (EUQ). For example, the EUR for external walls is the total cost of the external walls divided by EUQ for external walls. EURs include all the cost of all materials, labour, plant, *subcontractor's preliminaries*, *subcontractor's* design fees and *subcontractor's* overheads and profit. EURs exclude *main contractor's preliminaries*, *main contractor's overheads and profit* and other allowances, such as *project/design team fees*, *other development/project costs*, *risk allowances* and *inflation*. These items are to be assessed separately.

Elemental cost analysis (or **cost analysis**) – is a full appraisal of costs involved in previously constructed buildings and is aimed mainly at providing reliable information which will assist in accurately estimating cost of future buildings. It provides a product-based cost model, providing data on which initial elemental estimates and *elemental cost plans* can be based.

Elemental cost plan (or **cost plan**) – is the critical breakdown of the *cost limit* for the building(s) into *cost targets* for each *element* of the building(s). It provides a statement of how the *design team* proposes to distribute the available budget among the *elements* of the building, and a frame of reference from which to develop the design and maintain *cost control*. It also provides both a work breakdown structure (WBS) and a cost breakdown structure (CBS) which, by codifying, can be used to redistribute work in *elements* to construction works packages for the purpose of procurement.

Elemental method – is a budget setting technique which considers the major *elements* of a building and provides an *order of cost estimate* based on an elemental breakdown of a building project. The *elemental method* can also be used to develop an initial cost model as a prerequisite to developing an *elemental cost plan*. The method involves the use of *element unit quantities* (EUQ) and *element unit rates* (EUR).

Employer – means the owner and/or the developer of the building; in some cases the ultimate user. The terms Senior Responsible Owner (SRO) and Project Sponsor are used by central civil government and the defence sector; being the representatives empowered to manage the building project and make project specific decisions. For the purpose of these measurement rules, the term employer shall also mean Senior Responsible Owner (SRO) or Project Sponsor.

Estimate base date – means the date on which the *cost limit* (excluding *inflation* – i.e. the sum of the *works cost estimate*, *project/design team fees estimate*, *other development/project costs* estimate and *risk allowance* estimate) is established as a basis for calculating *inflation*, changes or other related variances.

Formal Cost Plan – is the elemental cost plan which is reported to the employer on completion of a specific *RIBA Work Stage* or *OGC Gateway*.

Formal Cost Plan stage – is the point at which the quantity surveyor/cost manager formally submits an *elemental cost plan* to the *employer* for consideration. The formal cost plan stages are interlinked with the appropriate *RIBA Work Stages* and *OGC Gateways*.

Functional unit – means a unit of measurement used to represent the prime use of a building or part of a building (e.g. per bed space, per house and per m² of retail area). It also includes all associated circulation space.

Functional unit method – is a rough budget setting technique which consists of selecting a suitable standard *functional unit* of use for the project, and multiplying the projected number of units by an appropriate cost per *functional unit*.

Gross external area (GEA) – is the area of a building measured externally (i.e. to the external face of the perimeter walls) at each floor level. The rules of measurement of gross external floor area are defined in the *RICS Code of Measuring Practice* (6th edition).

Gross internal floor area (GIFA) (or **gross internal area (GIA)**) – is the area of a building measured to the internal face of the perimeter walls at each floor level. The rules of measurement of gross internal floor area are defined in the *RICS Code of Measuring Practice* (6th edition). Refer to Appendix A of these rules.

Group element – means the main headings used to describe the facets of an *elemental cost plan* (i.e. Substructure; Superstructure; Internal finishes; Fittings, furnishings and equipment; Services; Complete buildings and building units; Work to existing buildings; External works; Facilitating works; Main contractor's preliminaries; Main contractor's overheads and profit; Project/design team fees; Other development/project costs; Risks; and Inflation).

Inflation – means an allowance included in the *order of cost estimate* or *cost plan* for fluctuations in the basic prices of labour, plant and equipment and materials. Refer to definitions for *tender inflation* and *construction inflation*.

Main contractor (or **prime contractor**) – means the contractor responsible for the total construction and completion process of the building project. The term prime contractor is often used to mean main contractor in central civil government and the defence sector.

Main contractor's overheads and profit – means the *main contractor's* costs associated with head office administration proportioned to each building contract plus the *main contractor's* return on capital investment. *Main contractor's preliminaries* exclude costs associated with *subcontractor's* overheads and profit, which are to be included in the *unit rates* applied to building works.

Main contractor's preliminaries – are items which cannot be allocated to a specific *element*, *sub-element* or *component*. *Main contractor's preliminaries* include the *main contractor's* costs associated with management and staff, site establishment, temporary services, security, safety and environmental protection, control and protection, common user mechanical plant, common user temporary works, the maintenance of site records, completion and post-completion requirements, cleaning, fees and charges, sites services and insurances, bonds, guarantees and warranties. *Main contractor's preliminaries* exclude costs associated with *subcontractor's preliminaries*, which are to be included in the *unit rates* applied to building works.

Net internal area (NIA) – is the usable area within a building measured to the internal face of the perimeter walls at each floor level. The rules of measurement of *net internal area* are defined in the *RICS Code of Measuring Practice* (6th edition). Refer to Appendix C of these rules.

OGC Gateway Process – is a process that examines programmes and projects at key decision points in their lifecycle. It looks ahead to provide assurance that the *employer* can progress to the next stage. Project reviews are carried under *OGC Gateway* reviews 1 to 5. Typically a project will undergo three reviews before a commitment to invest, and two looking at service implementation and confirmation of the operational benefits. The process is best practice in central civil government, the health sector, local government and the defence sector. The emphasis of the *OGC Gateway Process* is to examine the business case, which requires an assessment of the *total development cost* of the building project.

OGC Gateways (or OGC Gateway) – are key decision points within the *OGC Gateway Process*.

Option cost – is an estimate of the cost of alternative design solutions to achieve the *employer's* objectives; so that they can be compared and appraised. *Option costs* will be incorporated in the overarching cost report.

Order of cost estimate – means the determination of possible cost of a building(s) early in design stage in relation to the *employer's* fundamental requirements. This takes place prior to preparation of full set of working drawings or bills of quantities and forms the initial build-up to the *cost planning* process.

Other development/project costs – means costs that are not necessarily directly associated with the cost of constructing the building, but form part of the total cost of the building project to the *employer* (e.g. land acquisition costs, fees for letting agents, marketing costs and contributions associated with Section 106 Agreements).

Overheads and profit – See definition for *main contractor's overheads and profit*.

Preliminaries – See definition for *main contractor's preliminaries*.

Prime cost sum (PC Sum) – means a sum of money included in a *unit rate* to be expended on materials or goods from suppliers (e.g. ceramic wall tiles at £36.00/m² or door furniture at £75.00/door). It is a supply only rate for materials or goods where the precise quality of those materials and goods are unknown. PC Sums exclude all costs associated with fixing or installation, all ancillary and sundry materials and goods required for the fixing or installation of the materials or goods, *subcontractor's* design fees, *subcontractor's preliminaries*, *subcontractor's* overheads and profit, *main contractor's* design fees, *main contractor's preliminaries* and *main contractor's overheads and profit*.

Project team – means *employer*, project manager, quantity surveyor/cost manager, *design team* and all other consultants responsible for the delivery of the building project on time, on cost and to the required performance criteria (design and quality). The *project team* will include the *main contractor* where the *main contractor* has been engaged by the *employer* to provide pre-construction services.

Project/design team fee(s) – means *project team* and *design team* consultants' fees for pre-construction, construction and post construction related services, other consultants' fees, fees and charges for intrusive site investigations, specialist support consultants' fees and main contractor's fees for the provision of pre-construction services. See group element 12: Project/design team fees for an indicative list of *project/design team fees*.

Project/design team fees estimate – means the total estimated cost of all *project/design team fees* at the *estimate base date* (i.e. excluding *tender inflation* and *construction inflation*).

Residual risk (or retained risk) – means the risks retained by the *employer*.

Retail area – means the net internal area (NIA). The rules of measurement of retail area of a shop are defined in the *RICS Code of Measuring Practice* (6th edition). Refer to Appendix D of these rules.

RIBA Outline Plan of Work – summarises the deliverables required under each *RIBA Work Stage*.

RIBA Plan of Work – is a model procedure dealing with basic steps in decision making for a medium-sized building project. The *RIBA Plan of Work* sets out a logical structure for building projects, starting with the brief and ending with post-occupancy evaluation. The procedures identify the responsibilities of the *design team* at each stage of the design and contract administration process. Each step is referred to as a *RIBA Work Stage*. The full title of the *RIBA Plan of Work* is *The Architect's Plan of Work*, published by RIBA, but it is commonly known and referred to as the *RIBA Plan of Work* in the building construction industry.

RIBA Work Stage (or RIBA Work Stages) – means the stage into which the process of designing building projects and administering building contracts may be divided. Some variations of the *RIBA Work Stages* apply for design and build procurement.

Risk allowance – means the amount added to the *base cost estimate* for items that cannot be precisely predicted to arrive at the *cost limit*.

Risk register (or **risk log**) – means a schedule of identified risks.

Risk value – means an estimate of the cost of the individual risk.

Site area – means the total area of the site within the site title boundaries (or the total area within the site title boundaries defined by the *employer* as the site for the building), measured on a horizontal plane, excluding the area of the building footprint. Excludes any areas used temporarily for the building works that do not form part of the delivered building project.

Subcontractor – means a contractor who undertakes specific work within the building project; known as specialist, works, trade, work package, and labour only *subcontractors*.

Subcontractor's preliminaries – are preliminaries that relate specifically to building work which is to be carried out by a *subcontractor*. Costs associated with *subcontractor's preliminaries* are to be included in the *unit rates* applied to *sub-elements* and individual *components*.

Sub-element – means a part of an *element*. Similar to *elements*, a separate *cost target* can be established for each *sub-element*.

Tender inflation – means an allowance included in the *order of cost estimate* or *cost plan* for fluctuations in the basic prices of labour, plant and equipment and materials during the period from the *estimate base date* to the date of tender return. See also the definition for *construction inflation*.

Total development cost – means the *cost limit* (including *inflation* – i.e. the total of the *works cost estimate*, the *project/design team fees estimate*, *other development/project costs* estimates, *tender inflation* and *construction inflation*) for the building project.

Unit rate(s) – means the monetary rate applied to an *element*, *sub-element* or *component* per unit of measurement (e.g. cost per m, cost per m² and cost per m³). The term also includes *costs/m² of GIFA* and *cost per functional unit* (or *functional unit cost*).

Works cost estimate – means the combined total estimated cost of the *building works estimate*, the *main contractor's preliminaries* and the *main contractor's overheads and profit* prepared using prices current at the time the estimate is prepared (or updated). The *works cost estimate* contains no allowance for *project/design team fees*, *other development/project costs*, *risk allowances*, *tender inflation* and *construction inflation*.

Part 2: Measurement rules for order of cost estimating

Part 2: Measurement rules for order of cost estimating

2.1 Introduction

2.1.1 Part 2 of the rules describes the purpose and content of an *order of cost estimate*, puts *order of cost estimates* in context with the *RIBA Plan of Work* and *OGC Gateway Process*, and sets out the rules of measurement for the preparation of *order of cost estimates* using the following estimating methods:

(a) floor area method;

(b) *functional unit method* (e.g. per bed space, per house type and per m² of *retail area*); and

(c) *elemental method* (i.e. individual *elements*).

2.1.2 The content and application of *unit rates* (i.e. *costs/m² of GIFA*, functional unit rates and *element unit rates* (EURs)) to measured quantities to generate the base cost of the *building works* is also described; together with the method of dealing with cost allowances for *main contractor's preliminaries*, *main contractor's overheads and profit*, *project/design team fees*, *other development/project costs*, *risk allowances*, *inflation* and Value Added Tax (VAT).

2.1.3 In addition, the basic information requirements needed (from the *employer* and other *project team* members) by the quantity surveyor/cost manager to complete *order of cost estimates* are outlined. The essential content of the quantity surveyor's/cost manager's *order of cost estimate* report to the *employer* is also described.

2.1.4 The rules of measurement for *element unit quantities* used for the *elemental method* of estimating can also be used as a basis for measuring *element unit quantities* (EUQs) for the cost analysis of building projects.

2.2 Purpose of an order of cost estimate

2.2.1 *Order of cost estimates* are produced as an intrinsic part of *RIBA Work Stages* A: Appraisal and B: Design Brief, or *OGC Gateways* 1 (Business Justification) and 2 (Delivery Strategy). The requirements of *RIBA Work Stages* A and B, as described in the *RIBA Outline Plan of Work*, are as follows:

(a) *RIBA Work Stage* A: Appraisal

'Identification of [employer's] needs and objectives, business case and possible constraints on development. Preparation of feasibility studies and assessment of options to enable the [employer] to decide whether to proceed.'

OGC Gateway 1 (Business Justification) can be compared with *RIBA Work Stage* A.

(b) *RIBA Work Stage* B: Design Brief

'Development of initial statement of requirements into the Design Brief by or on behalf of the [employer] confirming key requirements and constraints. Identification of procurement method, procedures, organisational structure and range of consultants and others to be engaged for the project.'

OGC Gateway 2 (Delivery Strategy) can be compared with *RIBA Work Stage* B.

Project stages from the *RIBA Outline Plan of Work 2007*, copyright Royal Institute of British Architects, are reproduced here with the permission of the RIBA.

2.2.2 The purpose of an *order of cost estimate* is to establish if the proposed building project is affordable and, if affordable, to establish a realistic *cost limit* for the building project. The *cost limit* is the maximum expenditure that the *employer* is prepared to make in relation to the completed building project, which will be managed by the *project team* (i.e. *authorised budget*).

2.2.3 As part of *RIBA Work Stages* A and B or Gateways 1 and 2, it may be necessary to estimate the cost of a number of alternative building types or development scenarios for a site. Such alternative scenarios are known as *option costs* or *option costings*.

2.3 Information requirements for order of cost estimates

2.3.1 To enable preparation of an *order of cost estimate*, information will be required **from the employer** as follows:

(a) Location of the site and the availability of the site for commencement of the building project.

(b) A statement of building use.

(c) A statement of floor area (or number of *functional units*) and schedule of accommodation – in conjunction with the architect.

(d) Requirements for refurbishment (if the project comprises rehabilitation of an existing building) – in conjunction with the architect. Details of the new use and any outstanding maintenance or repairs necessary to give the building fabric the required life expectancy are required.

(e) Initial project/design brief, including statement of quality, sustainability requirements and 'fit-out' requirements – in conjunction with the architect.

(f) Details of any enabling works, decanting or other specific requirements.

(g) Indicative programme, including key dates (e.g. planning application and occupation dates).

(h) Details of any particular restraints to be imposed by the *employer*, local planners or statutory undertakers – in conjunction with the architect (e.g. work in a secure area, limitations on building position, work in a conservation area, work to a historic or listed building, external appearance and number of storeys).

(i) Details of any particular site conditions – in conjunction with the architect (e.g. sloping site, likelihood of contaminated ground, demolition of existing buildings, adequacy and condition of existing mains services).

(j) Budget/cash flow constraints.

(k) Initial views (if any) on construction procurement options and contract strategies.

(l) Life span (e.g. 10 year, 25 year or 60 year target life span).

(m) An indication of the proposed storey heights of the building – in conjunction with the architect. The introduction of raised access floors for IT cabling or deep suspended ceiling voids for mechanical and electrical services installations could significantly increase storey height, thus increasing estimated costs. Where such requirement is known, it is recommended that this is stated.

(n) Particular requirements in respect of mechanical and electrical services installations – in conjunction with the architect (and mechanical and electrical services engineer – if appointed).

(o) Requirements in respect of:

- treatment of project/design team fees;

- approach to other development/project costs'

- treatment of inflation; and

- treatment of Value Added Tax (VAT).

(p) Other considerations (e.g. approach to dealing with capital allowances, land remediation and grants).

2.3.2 To enable preparation of an *order of cost estimate*, information will be required **from the architect** as follows:

(a) Design study sketches or drawings for each alternative design/development option to a suitable scale, comprising:

- floor plans (for each different floor plate configuration/shape and use);
- roof plan(s);
- elevations; and
- sections.

(b) Schedule of *gross external areas* (GEA), *gross internal floor areas* (GIFA), *net internal areas* (NIA – i.e. usable area for shops, supermarkets and offices) and *site area* (SA).

(c) Minimum storey heights.

(d) Schedule of accommodation – in conjunction with the *employer*.

(e) Number of car parking spaces and whether above ground or below ground.

(f) Indicative specification/design intent for building option(s).

(g) Indicative environmental/sustainability strategy – in conjunction with the mechanical and electrical services engineer.

(h) Advice on likely site constraints.

(i) Advice on likely planning constraints.

(j) Definition of 'fit-out'.

(k) Initial *risk register/log*.

2.3.3 To enable preparation of an *order of cost estimate*, information will be required **from the mechanical and electrical services engineer** (if appointed) as follows:

(a) Indicative services specification/design intent for building option(s).

(b) Indicative environmental/sustainability strategy – in conjunction with the architect.

(c) Advice on availability and/or adequacy of utility services connections to the site.

(d) Initial *risk register/log*.

2.3.4 To enable preparation of an *order of cost estimate*, information will be required **from the structural engineer** (if appointed) as follows:

(a) Advice on probable ground conditions.

(b) Indicative services specification/design intent for building option(s).

(c) Initial *risk register/log*.

2.3.5 The accuracy of an *order of cost estimate* is dependent on the quality of the information supplied to the quantity surveyor/cost manager. The more information provided, the more reliable the outcome will be. Where little or no information is provided, the quantity surveyor/cost manager will need to qualify the *order of cost estimate* accordingly.

2.4   Constituents of an order of cost estimate

2.4.1   The key constituents of an *order of cost estimate* are as follows.

Constituent	
Building works estimate [1]	See paragraph 2.5
Main contractor's preliminaries estimate [2]	See paragraph 2.9
Sub-total [3] $[(3) = (1) + (2)]$	
Main contractor's overheads and profit estimate [4]	See paragraph 2.10
Works cost estimate [5] $[(5) = (3) + (4)]$	
Project/design team fees estimate (if required) [6]	See paragraph 2.11
Sub-total [7] $[(7) = (5) + (6)]$	
Other development/project costs estimate (if required) [8]	See paragraph 2.12
Base cost estimate [9] $[(9) = (7) + (8)]$	
Risk allowances estimate [10] $[(10) = (10(a)) + (10(b)) + (10(c)) + (10(d))]$	See paragraph 2.13
(a) Design development risks estimate [10(a)]	
(b) Construction risks estimate [10(b)]	
(c) Employer change risks estimate [10(c)]	
(d) Employer other risks estimate [10(d)]	
Cost limit (excluding inflation) [11] $[(11) = (9) + (10)]$	
Tender inflation estimate [12]	See paragraph 2.14
Cost limit (excluding construction inflation) [13] $[(13) = (11) + (12)]$	
Construction inflation estimate [14]	See paragraph 2.14
Cost limit (including inflation) [15] $[(15) = (13) + (14)]$	
VAT assessment	See paragraph 2.15

2.4.2   The *base cost estimate* is the total of the *building works estimate*, *main contractor's preliminaries* estimate and *main contractor's overheads and profit* estimate, *project/design team fee estimate* and the *other development/project costs* estimate. The *base cost estimate* is to contain no allowances for *risk* or *inflation*.

2.4.3   Allowances for *risk* and *inflation* are to be calculated separately and added the *base cost estimate* to determine the *cost limit* for the building project.

2.5   Measurement rules for building works

2.5.1   Quantities for *building works* shall be determined by measuring the total gross internal floor area (GIFA) of the building or buildings (using the *floor area method*) or by projecting the number of *functional units* (using the *functional unit method*). In certain circumstances, a combination of both floor area methods and *functional unit methods* may need to be employed.

    (a)   **Floor area method**

        (i)   The total *gross internal floor area* (GIFA) of the building or buildings is measured and multiplied by an appropriate *cost/m² of GIFA*. The equation for calculating the total estimated cost of *building works* is therefore:

$$c = a \times b$$

where:

a = GIFA

b = cost/m² of GIFA for building works

c = building works estimate (i.e. total estimated cost of building works)

(ii) The *gross internal floor area* (GIFA) is to be measured in accordance with the 'Core definition: gross internal area (GIA)' of the *RICS Code of Measuring Practice*, which is reproduced in Appendix A of these rules.

(iii) Where measurement is for more than one building, the measurement for each building is to be shown separately.

(iv) Where a single building comprises more than one user function (e.g. residential, retail and offices), then the GIFA of each function is to be calculated and quantified separately. The sum total of the GIFA for each separate function is to be equal to the GIFA for the whole building. For the purpose of establishing the GIFA of each separate building function, the centre line of the party wall shall be used to delineate the functions.

(v) Where the external works is to be measured separately, the *site area* (SA) is to be measured. The SA is the total area of the site within the site title boundaries (or the total area within the site title boundaries defined by the *employer* as the site for the building), excluding the footprint of the new building(s), measured on a horizontal plane.

(b) **Functional unit method**

(i) *Functional units* are a unit of measurement used to represent the prime use of a building or part of a building. Each *functional unit* includes all circulation necessary. It is essential that the *functional unit* is clearly identified when measurements are expressed in this way. A list of commonly used *functional units* and *functional units* of measurement for buildings is provided in Appendix B of these rules.

(ii) A suitable *functional unit* of use for the building is to be selected. The total number of *functional units* is determined and multiplied by an appropriate *cost per functional unit* (or *functional unit cost*). The equation for calculating the total estimated cost of *building works* is therefore:

c = a x b

where:

a = number of functional units

b = cost per functional unit (or functional unit cost)

c = building works estimate (i.e. total estimated cost of building works)

(iii) Where measurement for the *functional unit* is to be 'net internal area', the *net internal area* (NIA) is to be measured in accordance with the 'Core definition: net internal area (NIA)' of the *RICS Code of Measuring Practice*, which is reproduced in Appendix C of these rules.

(iv) Where measurement for the *functional unit* is to be expressed as 'retail area', the *retail area* of the shop is to be measured in accordance with the 'Special Use Definition: Shops' of the *RICS Code of Measuring Practice*, which is reproduced in Appendix D of these rules.

(v) A *functional unit* includes all circulation necessary.

(vi) Where the external works is to be measured separately, the *site area* (SA) is to be measured. The SA is the total area of the site within the site title boundaries (or the total area within the site title boundaries defined by the *employer* as the site for the building), excluding the footprint of the new building(s), measured on a horizontal plane.

2.6   Elemental method

2.6.1   The *elemental method* is an alternative approach for calculating the total estimated cost of *building works* (i.e. the *building works estimate*). The *elemental method* considers the major *elements* of a building and provides an *order of cost estimate* based on an elemental breakdown of the building project. Ordinarily, the *group elements* and *elements* used in the *elemental method* are the same as those used in the *elemental cost planning* process (see Parts 3 and 4 of these rules). However, the choice and number of *elements* used to break down the cost of *building works* will be dependent on the information available. The major *elements* commonly used when preparing an *order of cost estimate* using the *elemental method* are listed in the following table.

Group element	Element
1 Substructure	
2 Superstructure	2.1 Frame
	2.2 Upper floors
	2.3 Roof
	2.4 Stairs and ramps
	2.5 External walls
	2.6 Windows and external doors
	2.7 Internal walls and partitions
	2.8 Internal doors
3 Internal finishes	3.1 Wall finishes
	3.2 Floor finishes
	3.3 Ceiling finishes
4 Fittings, furnishings and equipment	
5 Services	5.1 Sanitary appliances
	5.2 Services equipment
	5.3 Disposal installations
	5.4 Water installations
	5.5 Heat source
	5.6 Space heating and air conditioning
	5.7 Ventilation systems
	5.8 Electrical installations
	5.9 Gas and other fuel installations
	5.10 Lift and conveyor installations
	5.11 Fire and lightning protection
	5.12 Communication, security and control systems
	5.13 Special installations
	5.14 Builders' work in connection with services
	5.15 Testing and commissioning of services
6 Complete buildings and building units	
7 Works to existing buildings	
8 External works	
9 Facilitating works	

Note: See *Appendix F: Logic and arrangement of levels 1 to 3 for elemental cost planning*, which provides a detailed list of all the *group elements* and *elements* used for *elemental cost planning*.

2.6.2   The method of measuring and the unit of measurement for each of the *elements* are set out in *Appendix E: Measurement rules for elemental method of estimating*.

2.6.3   If suitable information is available, then *element unit quantities* (EUQ) are measured for an *element* in accordance with the rules and priced with suitable *element unit rates* (EUR) to ascertain the *cost target* for an *element*. Where insufficient information is available for a particular *element*, the EUQ for the *element* is based on the GIFA. The equation for calculating the *cost target* for an *element* is therefore:

$$c = a \times b$$

where:

$$a = EUQ$$

$$b = EUR$$

$$c = \text{cost target (for element)}$$

2.6.4 The total estimated cost of *building works* (i.e. the *building works estimate*) is ascertained by adding together the *cost target* for each *element*. The equation for calculating the *building works estimate* using the *elemental method* is therefore:

$$b = \sum (a1 + a2 + a3 + a4 + a5 + a6 + a7 + a8 + a9)$$

where:

$$a1, a2, a3, \text{etc.} = \text{cost target for element}$$

$$b = \text{building works estimate}$$

2.6.5 Where measurement is to be based on the *gross internal floor area* (GIFA), the area is to be measured in accordance with the 'Core definition: gross internal floor area (GIA)' of the *RICS Code of Measuring Practice*, which is reproduced in Appendix A of these rules.

2.6.6 Where a building project comprises more than one building, the measurement for each building is to be shown separately.

2.6.7 The *elemental method* can also be used to generate an initial cost model (or an outline *elemental cost plan*) at the commencement of *RIBA Work Stage* C: Concept or *OGC Gateway* 3A: Design Brief and Concept Approval, whichever is applicable. This elemental breakdown provides a frame of reference from which Formal Cost Plan 1 can be developed (see Part 3 of these rules). The initial EUQs and EURs will eventually be superseded by more detailed measurement of *elements*, *sub-elements* and *components* and *unit rates* once suitable design information has been prepared and the *elemental cost plan* evolves.

2.6.8 The measurement rules for the *elemental method* of estimating in Appendix E of these rules can also be used as a basis for measuring *element unit quantities* (EUQs) for the purpose of *cost analysis* and benchmark analysis of building projects. The content of each *group* and *element* is defined in *Part 4: Tabulated rules of measurement for elemental cost planning*.

2.7 Unit rates and element unit rates (EURs) used to estimate the cost of building works

2.7.1 *Unit rates* applied to measured quantities are to be applicable to the method of measurement used (i.e. rates based on *cost/m² of GIFA* to be used for measured quantities determined using the floor area method, a *cost per functional unit* for measured quantities calculated using the *functional unit method* and appropriate *element unit rates* (EURs) where measured quantities are derived using the *elemental method*).

2.7.2 Both *unit rates* (i.e. *cost/m² of GIFA* or *cost per functional unit* (or *functional unit cost*)) and *element unit rates* (EURs) used to estimate the total cost of *building works* are to include the cost of all materials, labour and plant that are specifically required to construct the building or *element*. *Unit rates* and EURs are also to include allowances for any *subcontractors'* or suppliers' design fees, *subcontractors' preliminaries* and *subcontractors'* overheads and profit. *Unit rates* and EURs are to exclude allowances for *main contractor's preliminaries*, *main contractor's overheads and profit* and other allowances, such as *project/design team fees*, *other development/project costs*, *risk allowances* and *inflation*. These items are to be assessed separately and added to the estimated cost of *building works* (i.e. the *building works estimate*).

2.7.3   *Costs per functional unit* (or *functional unit costs*) include costs connected with all circulation space associated with the *functional unit*.

2.7.4   The *cost/m² of GIFA*, the *cost per functional unit* (or *functional unit cost*) and EURs can be interpolated from cost analyses or from benchmark analyses of previous buildings of a similar type. *Unit rates* ascertained from cost analyses or benchmark analyses of previous buildings should, if necessary, be adjusted to reflect changes in specification level between the previous building and the proposed building. Time and regional variation of costs should also be considered.

2.7.5   When using *unit rates* from cost analyses and benchmark analyses, it is recommended that such rates are adjusted to reflect prices current at the time the *order of cost estimate* is prepared (i.e. adjusted to remove allowances included for *construction inflation*). Consider the following scenario:

> A cost analysis is to be prepared on a building project, where:
>
> | | |
> |---|---|
> | *Tender return date:* | *7 December 2008* |
> | *Original contract sum (i.e. the agreed tender price):* | *£30,600,900* |
> | *Possession of the site (and commencement date of the contract period):* | *11 February 2009* |
> | *Contract period (i.e. construction period):* | *36 months (3 years)* |
> | *Date for completion:* | *10 February 2012* |
> | *Tender price index (TPI) to be stated in cost analysis:* | *December 2008 (or 4th quarter 2008)* |

Based on the above scenario, the original contract sum (and rates and prices within) will include an allowance by the *main contractor* for *construction inflation* (i.e. an allowance to cover the risks of *inflation* during the period from the 'tender return date' to the 'date for completion'). If no adjustment is made to the original contract sum (and rates and prices within) for *construction inflation* in the *cost analysis*, and the TPI is given as the 'tender return date', then there is a significant risk that a quantity surveyor/cost manager will over allow for *construction inflation* when developing an *order of cost estimate*. Therefore, it is recommended that all *construction inflation* is omitted from cost analyses and benchmark analyses data.

2.7.6   It is further recommended that cost analyses (and benchmark analyses) be based on the agreed tender price (i.e. the original contract sum); not on the final contract sum (i.e. the agreed final account sum). The two main reasons for this are:

(a)   The cost analysis (or benchmark analyses) would not be available until after the final account sum had been agreed, which could be three or four years after an analysis undertaken at tender stage.

(b)   It is much more difficult to analyse both the original contract sum and variation account than to analyse the original contract sum alone.

2.8   Updating unit rates and other costs to current estimate base date

2.8.1   The *estimate base date* is to be established for an *order of cost estimate*. It is essential, therefore, that the *unit rates* used from cost analyses and benchmark analyses are updated to bring them into line with the *estimate base date* established for the *order of cost estimate*.

2.8.2   To update a *unit rate* from cost analyses or benchmark analyses data to the current *estimate base date*, the *unit rate* is increased by the amount of inflation occurring during the period from the *base date of cost data* to the current *estimate base date*. The equation for calculating the updated *unit rate* is therefore:

$$Ra2 = Ra1 + (Ra1 \times p)$$

where:

Ra1 = unit rate at base date of cost data

Ra2 = unit rate at current estimate base date

p = percentage addition for inflation

The percentage addition for inflation (p) can be computed using published indices (i.e. tender price indices (TPI), building cost indices or retail price indices (RPI)). Alternatively, the percentage addition can be derived from in-house sources of indices. Using published indices, the equation for calculating the percentage addition for *inflation* is therefore:

$$p = ((index\ 2 - index\ 1) \div index\ 1) \times 100$$

where:

index 1 = index at base date of cost data

index 2 = index at current estimate base date

p = percentage addition for inflation

Note: Care should be taken not to update previous rates that were based on percentage additions (e.g. *main contractor's preliminaries, main contractor's overheads and profit* and *project/design team fees*). Such items will be systematically updated when the percentage addition is applied to the updated *unit rates* (and other rates).

2.9 Cost estimate for main contractor's preliminaries

2.9.1 *Main contractor's preliminaries* are to be added as a percentage to the total cost of *building works* (i.e. to the *building works estimate*). The percentage addition to be applied for *main contractor's preliminaries* can be derived from a properly considered assessment of cost analyses of previous building projects. The percentage can be ascertained by calculating the *main contractor's preliminaries* as a percentage of the total cost of all *elements* forming the *building works*. Benchmark data from previously completed building projects can also be used to assess the level of *main contractor's preliminaries* to be applied to a new building project.

2.9.2 The estimated cost of *main contractor's preliminaries* is to be calculated by applying the selected percentage addition for *main contractor's preliminaries* to the cost of the *building works*. The equation for calculating the total estimated cost of *main contractor's preliminaries* is therefore:

$$c = a \times p$$

where:

a = building works estimate (i.e. total estimated cost of building works)

p = percentage for main contractor's preliminaries

c = main contractor's preliminaries estimate (i.e. total estimated cost of main contractor's preliminaries)

2.9.3 The *main contractor's preliminaries* estimate is added to the *building works estimate*.

2.9.4 If known at this early stage, costs relating to known site constraints, special construction methods, sequencing of works or other non-standard requirements are to be assessed and identified separately.

2.9.5 Allowance for *subcontractors' preliminaries*, design fees, *risk allowances* and overheads and profit are to be incorporated in the *cost/m² of GIFA, cost per functional unit* (or *functional unit cost*) or *element unit rates* (EURs) used to estimate the cost of building works (i.e. to calculate the *building works estimate*).

2.9.6 A list of typical items found within *main contractor's preliminaries*, is provided at *Part 4: Tabulated rules of measurement for elemental cost planning* (group element 10: Main contractor's preliminaries). This list is not meant to be definitive or exhaustive, but is simply a guide.

2.10 Cost estimate for main contractor's overheads and profit

2.10.1   *Main contractor's overheads and profit* is to be based on a percentage addition. The estimated cost of any *main contractor's overheads and profit* is to be calculated by applying the selected percentage addition for overheads and profit to the combined total cost of the *building works estimate* and the *main contractor's preliminaries* estimate. The equation for calculating the total estimated cost of *main contractor's overheads and profit* is therefore:

$$c = (a + b) \times p$$

where:

a = building works estimate (i.e. total estimated cost of building works)

b = main contractor's preliminaries estimate (i.e. total estimated cost of main contractor's preliminaries)

p = percentage for main contractor's overheads and profit

c = main contractor's overheads and profit estimate (i.e. total estimated cost of main contractor's overheads and profit)

2.10.2   The percentage addition to be applied for *main contractor's overheads and profit* is to be derived from a properly considered assessment of *main contractor's overheads and profit* found on previous building projects.

2.10.3   The *main contractor's overheads and profit* estimate is added to the combined total of the *building works estimate* and the *main contractor's preliminaries* estimate. This gives the *works cost estimate*. The equation for calculating the *works cost estimate* is therefore:

$$d = a + b + c$$

where:

a = building works estimate

b = main contractor's preliminaries estimate

c = main contractor's overheads and profit estimate

d = works cost estimate

2.10.4   A typical list of items to be found within *main contractor's overheads and profit*, is provided at *Part 4: Tabulated rules of measurement for elemental cost planning* (group element 11: Main contractor's overheads and profit). This list is not meant to be definitive or exhaustive, but is simply a guide.

2.11 Project/design team fees

2.11.1   *Project/design team fees* are the fees associated with the *project/design team* and other specialist consultants required for the building project. *Project/design team fees* may also include *main contractor's* pre-construction fees. A typical list of *project/design team fees*, including items to be found within *main contractor's* pre-construction fees, is provided at *Part 4: Tabulated rules of measurement for elemental cost planning* (group element 12: Project/design team fees). This list is not meant to be definitive or exhaustive, but is simply a guide.

2.11.2   *Project/design team fees* are to be included in *order of cost estimates* unless specifically excluded at the request of the *employer*.

2.11.3   It is recommended that a single allowance be made for *project/design team fees*.

2.11.4 For the purpose of *order of cost estimates*, it is recommended that *project/design team fees* be based on a percentage addition. *Project/design team fees* are to be calculated by applying the selected percentage addition for *project/design team fees* to the *works cost estimate*. The equation for calculating *project/design team fees* is therefore:

$$c = a \times p$$

where:

a = works cost estimate

p = percentage for project/design team fees

c = project/design team fees estimate (i.e. total estimated cost of project/design team fees)

2.11.5 The *project/design team fee estimate* is added to the *works cost estimate*.

2.12 Other development/project costs

2.12.1 *Other development/project costs* are for costs that are not necessarily directly associated with the works costs or *project/design team fees*, but form part of the total cost of the building project to the *employer* (for example, insurances, planning fees, fees in connection with party wall awards, decanting and relocation costs, marketing costs and contributions associated with Section 106 and Section 278 Agreements). Examples of *other development/project costs* are provided in *Part 4: Tabulated rules of measurement for elemental cost planning* (group element 13: Other development/project costs). These examples do not provide a definitive or exhaustive lost of items, but are simply a guide.

2.12.2 *Other development/project costs* are to be included in *order of cost estimates* unless specifically excluded at the request of the *employer*. *Other development/project costs* are to be added as a lump sum allowance.

2.12.3 The nature of *other development/project costs* and the extent of the lump sum allowance to be included in the *order of cost estimate* are to be ascertained in conjunction with the *employer*.

2.12.4 The total estimated cost of *other development/project costs* is added to the combined total of the *works cost estimate* and the *project/design team fees estimate*.

2.12.5 The combined total of the *works cost estimate*, the *project/design team fees estimate* and the *other development/project costs* estimate is the *base cost estimate*.

2.13 Risk allowances

2.13.1 All building projects involve risks, some obvious some less so; the proper management of risk saves time and money. Risks can occur at any point in a building project and it is essential that they are identified, assessed, monitored and controlled.

2.13.2 Risk exposure (i.e. the potential effect of risk) changes as the building project progresses; continually managing the risks is therefore essential. As the design evolves, more of the project requirements are defined, and a risk response can be decided. For example:

(a) **Risk avoidance**: where risks have such serious consequences on the project outcome that they are totally unacceptable. Risk avoidance measures might include a review of the *employer's* brief and a reappraisal of the project, perhaps leading to an alternative development mix, alternative design solution or its cancellation.

(b) **Risk reduction**: where the level of risk is unacceptable. Typical action to reduce risk can take the form of:

(i) Redesign: combined with improved value engineering.

(ii) More detailed design or further site investigation: to improve the information on which cost estimates and programmes are based.

(iii)   Different materials or engineering services: to avoid new technology or unproven systems or long delivery items.

(iv)   Different methods of construction: to avoid inherently risky construction techniques.

(v)   Changing the project execution plan: to package the work content differently, or to carry out enabling works.

(vi)   Changing the contract strategy: to allocate risk between the project participants in a different way.

(c)   **Risk transfer**: where accepting the risk would not give the *employer* best value for money. The object of transferring risk is to pass the responsibility to another party able to better control the risk. Whenever risk is transferred there is usually a premium to be paid (i.e. the receiving party's valuation of the cost of the risk). To be worthwhile, risk transfer should give better overall value for money to the *employer* (the total cost of the risk to the *employer* is reduced by more than the cost of the risk premium). Risk transfer measures include taking out insurance cover where appropriate.

(d)   **Risk sharing**: occurs when risk is not entirely transferred and the *employer* retains some element of risk.

(e)   **Risk retention**: risks retained by the *employer* that are not necessarily controllable. This remaining risk is called the *residual risk* exposure.

2.13.3   Considering the limited information about the building project and site conditions, the *risk allowance* at the *RIBA* Preparation *Work Stage* (i.e. A: Appraisal and B: Design Brief) and the *OGC* Business Justification and Delivery Strategy *Gateways* can be a significant percentage of the total estimated cost; whereas, after completion (when all accounts are settled) the requirement for a *risk allowance* will be zero. Proper risk identification, assessment, monitoring and control are therefore a prerequisite of realistic cost estimates and of minimising the consequential costs arising from the *employer's residual risk* exposure.

2.13.4   It is recommended that *risk allowances* are not a standard percentage, but a properly considered assessment of the risk, taking into account the completeness of the design and other uncertainties such as the amount of site investigation done.

2.13.5   It is recommended that separate allowances be made for each of the following:

(a)   **Design development risks** – an allowance for use during the design process to provide for the risks associated with design development, changes in estimating data, third party risks (e.g. planning requirements, legal agreements, covenants, environmental issues and pressure groups), statutory requirements, procurement methodology and delays in tendering.

(b)   **Construction risks** – an allowance for use during the construction process to provide for the risks associated with site conditions (e.g. access restrictions/limitations, existing buildings, boundaries, and existing occupants and users), ground conditions, existing services and delays by statutory undertakers.

(c)   **Employer change risks** – an allowance for use during both the design process and the construction process to provide for the risks of *employer* driven changes (e.g. changes in scope of works or brief, changes in quality and changes in time).

(d)   **Employer other risks** – an allowance for other *employer* risks (e.g. early handover, postponement, acceleration, availability of funds, liquidated damages or premiums on other contracts due to late provision of accommodation, unconventional tender action and special contract arrangements).

2.13.6   Lists of typical risks for each category of risk are at *Part 4: Tabulated rules of measurement for elemental cost planning (group element* 14: Risk allowances). These lists are not meant to be definitive or exhaustive, but are simply a guide.

2.13.7   *Risk allowances* are to be included in the *order of cost estimates*. Even at the *RIBA* Preparation *Work Stage* and the *OGC* Business Justification and Delivery Strategy *Gateways*, it is recommended that the size of the initial *risk allowance* is based on the results of a formal risk analysis. If the risk characteristics are not acceptable to the *employer*, it is advisable that the *risk allowance* is not determined until management action has been taken to review the *employer's* risk exposure and to identify suitable risk responses that will reduce this exposure to an acceptable level. It is recommended that a revised risk analysis is undertaken to determine the most likely out-turn cost and the *risk allowance*.

2.13.8 Throughout the *RIBA* Preparation *Work Stage* and the *OGC* Business Justification and Delivery Strategy *Gateways* of a building project, it is advisable that effort is concentrated upon the main sources of risk. It may be beneficial, even at this stage of the project, to prepare a project specific *risk register* incorporating the major risks identified and a risk management strategy. It is recommended that risks are not excluded without due consideration. Take care not to allow the natural optimism which surrounds the early stages of a building project to influence the realism of judgments which are to be made.

2.13.9 The risks which can influence the cost of a project change as the building project progresses through the subsequent *RIBA Work Stages*. It is recommended that risk registers and risk estimates are reassessed at regular intervals throughout the various formal stages of *cost planning* which follow once the *cost limit* has been authorised by the *employer*.

2.13.10 For the purpose of *order of cost estimates*, *risk allowances* for design development risks, construction risks and *employer's* risks based on the application of percentage additions are to be calculated by multiplying the *base cost estimate* by the selected percentage additions. The equation for calculating the *risk allowances* for design development risk, construction risk and *employer's* risk are therefore:

for design development risks: $R1 = a \times p1$

for construction risks: $R2 = a \times p2$

for employer change risks: $R3 = a \times p3$

for employer other risks: $R4 = a \times p4$

where:

a = base cost estimate

$p1$ = percentage risk allowance for design development risks

$p2$ = percentage risk allowance for construction risks

$p3$ = percentage risk allowance for employer change risks

$p4$ = percentage risk allowance for employer other risks

$R1$ = risk allowance estimate for design development risks (i.e. total estimated cost of risk allowance for design development risks)

$R2$ = risk allowance estimate for construction risks (i.e. total estimated cost of risk allowance for construction risks)

$R3$ = risk allowance estimate for employer change risks (i.e. total estimated cost of risk allowance for employer change risks)

$R4$ = risk allowance estimate for employer other risks (i.e. total estimated cost of risk allowance for employer other risks)

2.13.11 The equation for calculating the total *risk allowance* estimate is therefore:

$RA = R1 + R2 + R3 + R4$

where:

$R1$ = risk allowance estimate for design development risks

$R2$ = risk allowance estimate for construction risks

$R3$ = risk allowance estimate for employer change risks

$R4$ = risk allowance estimate for employer other risks

RA = risk allowances estimate

2.13.12 The *risk allowance* estimate is added to the *base cost estimate*. This gives the proposed *cost limit* (excluding *inflation*). The equation for calculating the *cost limit* (excluding *inflation*) is therefore:

$$CL = a + b$$

where:

a = base cost estimate

b = risk allowances estimate

CL = cost limit (excluding inflation)

2.14 Inflation

2.14.1 An *order of cost estimates* is to be prepared using prices current at the time the estimate is prepared. However, it is also necessary to consider possible future effects of *inflation*. That is price escalation:

(a)   to date of tender (i.e. *tender inflation*); and

(b)   during the construction period (i.e. *construction inflation*).

2.14.2 For the purpose of *order of cost estimates*, the period used to ascertain the effects of *inflation* are as follows:

(a)   *Tender inflation*: the period from the *estimate base date* to the date of tender return.

(b)   *Construction inflation*: the period from the date of tender return to the mid-point of the construction period.

2.14.3 For the purpose of *order of cost estimates*, a simple approach can be used to ascertain the amount *tender inflation* and *construction inflation* to be included.

2.14.4   **Tender inflation:** The amount of *tender inflation* is ascertained by applying a single percentage rate for *tender inflation* to the *cost limit* (excluding *inflation*). The addition of *tender inflation* gives the projected *cost limit* (excluding *construction inflation*) for the building project. The equation for calculating the amount of *tender inflation* is therefore:

$$t = CL \times p$$

where:

CL = cost limit (excluding inflation)

p = percentage for tender inflation

t = tender inflation estimate

The percentage for *tender inflation* (p) can be computed using published indices (i.e. tender price indices (TPI), building cost indices or retail price indices (RPI)). Alternatively, the percentage addition can be derived from in-house sources of indices.

2.14.5 The *tender inflation* estimate is added to the *cost limit* (excluding *inflation*). This gives the proposed *cost limit* (excluding *construction inflation*). The equation for calculating the *cost limit* (excluding *construction inflation*) is therefore:

$$CL2 = CL1 + t$$

where:

CL1 = cost limit (excluding inflation)

CL2 = cost limit (excluding construction inflation)

t = tender inflation estimate

2.14.6   **Construction inflation:** The amount of *construction inflation* is ascertained by applying a single percentage rate for *construction inflation* to the *cost limit* (excluding *construction inflation*). The addition of *construction inflation* gives the projected *cost limit* (including *inflation*) for the building project. The equation for calculating the amount of *construction inflation* is therefore:

$$c = CL \times p$$

where:

CL = cost limit (excluding construction inflation)

p = percentage for construction inflation

c = construction inflation estimate

The percentage for *construction inflation* (p) can be computed using published indices (i.e. tender price indices (TPI), building cost indices or retail price indices (RPI)). Alternatively, the percentage addition can be derived from in-house sources of indices.

2.14.7 The *construction inflation estimate* is added to the *cost limit* (excluding *inflation*). This gives the proposed *cost limit* (including *inflation*). The equation for calculating the *cost limit* (including *inflation*) is therefore:

$$CL2 = CL1 + c$$

where:

CL1 = cost limit (excluding construction inflation)

CL2 = cost limit (including inflation)

c = construction inflation estimate

Note: Care should be taken to ensure that the rates used to calculate an *order of cost estimate* that were derived from cost analyses or benchmark analyses have been adjusted to reflect prices current at the time the *order of cost estimate* is prepared (i.e. adjusted to remove allowances included for *construction inflation*). Refer to paragraph 2.7.5 of these rules.

2.14.8 It is recommended that potential cost increases caused by tendering conditions and the effects of changes in the market are also considered, such as price increases associated with particular materials or products or the impact of major projects sapping resources (home and abroad); particular specialist, works, trade, work package, and labour only *subcontractors*; or other countries buying major quantities of raw materials (e.g. China). However, it is recommended that such potential cost increases caused by tendering conditions and the effects of changes in the market be initially dealt with under *risk allowances*.

2.15 Value Added Tax (VAT) assessment

2.15.1 Value Added Tax (VAT) in relation to buildings is a complex area. Therefore, it is recommended that VAT be excluded from *order of cost estimates*.

2.15.2 It is recommended that specialist advice is sought on VAT matters to ensure that the correct rates are applied to the various aspects of a building project.

2.16 Other considerations

2.16.1 Other considerations include:

(a)   capital allowances for taxation purposes;

(b)   land remediation relief; and

(c)   grants.

2.16.2 Taxation allowances, taxation relief and grants can provide valuable financial aid to an *employer* on certain types of building project. However, it is recommended that specialist advice is sought to maximise the availability and quantum of capital allowances, land remediation relief and grants. For that reason, it is recommended that allowances in connection with capital allowances, land remediation relief and grants be excluded from *order of cost estimates*.

2.17 Reporting of order of cost estimates

2.17.1   Costs are to be expressed as '*cost/m² of GIFA (gross internal floor area)*'.

2.17.2   Where appropriate and/or required by an *employer*, costs may be expressed as a '*cost per functional unit*' (or '*functional unit cost*') as an alternative to, or in addition to, the *cost/m² of GIFA*. The *functional unit* may be an *employer* defined unit. It is essential, therefore, that the *functional unit* is clearly identified when costs are expressed in this way.

2.17.3   *Order of cost estimates*, as with all estimates, are to be of forecast out-turn cost, with stated allowances for *project/design team fees*, *other development/project costs*, *risk allowances*, *inflation* and VAT as appropriate.

2.17.4   Items included in and excluded from the estimated cost are to be clearly communicated to the *employer* when reporting the *order of cost estimate*.

2.17.5   Typical items to be included in *order of cost estimates* reports are:
(a)   project title;
(b)   project description;
(c)   a statement of cost (including *cost limit*);
(d)   details of the information and specification on which the *cost plan* was prepared;
(e)   a statement of the floor areas;
(f)   basis of cost estimates (i.e. assumptions);
(g)   *estimate base date* (i.e. to which *inflation* has been applied);
(h)   estimated costs of and a request for decisions on any alternative proposals (i.e. summary of *option costs*); and
(i)   inclusions and exclusions (i.e. a clear and unambiguous statement of what is included in and excluded from the *order of cost estimate*).

Part 3: Measurement rules for elemental cost planning

Part 3: Measurement rules for elemental cost planning

3.1 Introduction

3.1.1 Part 3 of the rules describes the purpose and content of *elemental cost plans* and explains the rules of measurement for the preparation of *formal cost plans*. The formal *cost planning* stages are also put in context with the *RIBA Plan of Work* and the *OGC Gateway Process*.

3.1.2 The content and application of *unit rates* to measured quantities to generate the base cost of the *building works* is also described; together with the method of dealing with cost allowances for *main contractor's preliminaries*, *main contractor's overheads and profit*, *project/design team fees*, *other development/project costs*, *risk allowances*, *inflation*, Value Added Tax (VAT) and capital allowances.

3.1.3 In addition, the basic information requirements needed (from the *employer* and other *project team* members) by the quantity surveyor/cost manager to complete *elemental cost plan* are outlined. The essential content of the quantity surveyor's/cost manager's cost reports to the *employer* is also described.

3.1.4 The measurement rules for *elemental cost planning* can also be used as a basis for measuring quantities for the application to whole life cycle costing.

3.2 Purpose of elemental cost planning

3.2.1 *Elemental cost plans* are produced as an intrinsic part of *RIBA Work Stages* C: Concept, D: Design Development, E: Technical Design and F: Production Information; or, when the *OGC Gateway Process* is used, Gateways 3A (Design Brief and Concept Approval) and 3B (Detailed Design Approval). The requirements of *RIBA Work Stages* C, D, E and F, as described in the *RIBA Outline Plan of Work*, are as follows:

(a) *RIBA Work Stage* C: Concept:

'Implementation of Design Brief and preparation of additional data. Preparation of Concept Design including outline proposals for structural and building services systems, outline specifications and [Formal Cost Plan 1]. Review of procurement route.'

OGC Gateway 3A (Design Brief and Concept Approval) can be compared with *RIBA Work Stage* C.

(b) *RIBA Work Stage* D: Design Development:

'Development of concept design to include structural and building services systems, updated outline specifications and cost plan. Completion of Project Brief. Application for detailed planning permission.'

Note: Application for detailed planning permission may be moved to suit project requirements.

(c) *RIBA Work Stage* E: Technical Design:

'Preparation of technical design(s) and specifications, sufficient to co-ordinate components and elements of the project and information for statutory standards and construction safety.'

Note: Information for statutory standards and construction safety may be moved to suit project requirements.

OGC Gateway 3B (Detailed Design Approval) can be compared with *RIBA Work Stages* D and E.

(d)   *RIBA Work Stage* F: Production Information:

'F1 Preparation of production information in sufficient detail to enable a tender or tenders to be obtained. Application for statutory approvals.'

Note: Application for statutory approvals may be moved to suit project requirements.

'F2 Preparation of further information for construction required under the building contract.'

Note: Further information for construction may be moved to suit project requirements.

OGC Gateway 3B (Detailed Design Approval) can be compared with *RIBA Work Stages* D and E.

Project stages from the *RIBA Outline Plan of Work 2007*, copyright Royal Institute of British Architects, are reproduced here with the permission of the RIBA.

3.2.2   The main purpose of *elemental cost planning* is to:

(a)   ensure that *employers* are provided with value for money;

(b)   make *employers* and designers aware of the cost consequences of their desires and/or proposals;

(c)   provide advice to designers that enable them to arrive at practical and balanced designs within budget;

(d)   keep expenditure within the *cost limit* approved by the *employer*; and

(e)   provide robust cost information upon which the *employer* can make informed decisions.

3.2.3   *Elemental cost planning* (or *cost planning*) is a budget distribution technique that is implemented during the design stages of a building project. It involves a critical breakdown of the *cost limit* (i.e. the *employer's authorised budget*) for the building(s) into *cost targets* for each *element* of the building(s). *Cost targets* are the recommended expenditure for each *element* (e.g. substructure, frame, upper floors and roof).

3.2.4   The *elemental cost plan* (or *cost plan*) that results is a statement of how the *project team* proposes to distribute the available budget among the *elements* of the building. It provides a frame of reference from which to develop the design and maintain *cost control*. It also provides both a work breakdown structure (WBS) and a cost breakdown structure (CBS) which, by codifying, can be used to redistribute works in *elements* to construction works packages for the purpose of procurement.

3.2.5   *Elemental cost planning* is an iterative process, which is performed in steps of increasing detail as more design information becomes available.

3.3   Constituents of an elemental cost plan

3.3.1   The key constituents of an *elemental cost plan* are:

Constituent	
Building works estimate [1]	See paragraph 3.10
Main contractor's preliminaries estimate [2]	See paragraph 3.13
Sub-total [3] [(3) = (1) + (2)]	
Main contractor's overheads and profit estimate [4]	See paragraph 3.14
Works cost estimate [5] [(3) + (4)]	
Project/design team fee estimate [6] [(6) = (6(a)) + (6(b)) + (6(c))]	See paragraph 3.15
(a) Consultants' fees [6(a)]	
(b) Main contractor's pre-construction fee estimate (if applicable) [6(b)]	
(c) Main contractor's design fees estimate (if applicable) [6(c)]	
Sub-total [7] [(7) = (5) + (6)]	
Other development/project costs estimate [8]	See paragraph 3.16
Base cost estimate [9] [(9) = (7) + (8)]	
Risk allowances estimate [10] [(10) = (10(a)) + (10(b)) + (10(c)) + (10(d))]	See paragraph 3.17
(a) Design development risks estimate [10(a)]	
(b) Construction risks estimate [10(b)]	
(c) Employer change risks estimate [10(c)]	
(d) Employer other risks estimate [10(d)]	
Cost limit (excluding inflation) [11] [(11) = (9) + (10)]	
Tender inflation estimate [12]	See paragraph 3.18
Cost limit (excluding construction inflation) [13] [(13) = (11) + (12)]	
Construction inflation estimate [14]	See paragraph 3.18
Cost limit (including inflation) [15] [(15) = (13) + (14)]	
VAT assessment	See paragraph 3.19

3.3.2   The *base cost estimate* is the total estimated cost of the *building works, main contractor's preliminaries* and *main contractor's overheads and profit*. The *base cost estimate* is to contain no allowances for *risk* or *inflation*.

3.3.3   Allowances for *risk* and *inflation* are to be calculated separately and added the *base cost estimate* to determine the *cost limit* for the building project.

3.4   Formal cost planning stages

3.4.1   There are a number of formal *cost planning* stages, which are comparable with the *RIBA* Design and Pre-Construction *Work Stages* and *OGC Gateways* 3A (Design Brief and Concept Approval) and 3B (Detailed Design Approval) for a building project. The *employer* is required to 'approve' the *cost plan* on completion of each *RIBA Work Stage* before authorising commencement of the next *RIBA Work Stage*.

3.4.2   For most building projects, *formal cost plans* are be completed, and submitted to the *employer* for approval, for each of the following *RIBA Work Stages* or *OGC Gateways*:

Formal Cost Plan	RIBA Work Stage
1	C: Concept
2	D: Design Development
3	E: Technical Design
	F: Production Information

Formal Cost Plan	OGC Gateway
1	3A: Design Brief and Concept Approval
2 and 3	3B: Detailed Design Approval

3.4.3   Formal Cost Plan 1 is prepared at a point where the scope of work is fully defined and key criteria are specified but no detailed design has commenced. Formal Cost Plan 1 will provide the frame of reference for Formal Cost Plan 2. Likewise, Formal Cost Plan 2 will provide the frame of reference for Formal Cost Plan 3. Neither Formal Cost Plans 2 or 3 involve the preparation of a completely new *elemental cost plan*; they are progressions of the previous *formal cost plans*, which are developed through the *cost checking* of cost significant *components* and *cost targets* as more design information and further information about the site becomes available.

3.4.4   Whether or not a *formal cost plan* is prepared at each *RIBA Work Stage* or *OGC Gateway* is dependent on the procurement strategy selected. For example, the preparation of an updated *cost plan* might not be required at *Work Stage* F: Production Information where a design and build contract strategy is selected.

3.4.5   The *cost targets* within each *formal cost plan* approved by the *employer* will be used as the baseline for future cost comparisons. Each subsequent *cost plan* will require reconciliation with the preceding *cost plan* and explanations relating to changes made. In view of this, it is essential that records of any transfers made to or from the *risk allowances* and any adjustments made to *cost targets* are maintained, so that explanations concerning changes can be provided to both the *employer* and the *project team*.

3.4.6   To avoid unnecessary conflict, it is essential that *employers* and other *project/design team* members are aware of what is included in each *element* of the *cost plan*.

3.5 Reviewing and approving cost plans

3.5.1   Prior to the *employer* authorising commencement of the next *RIBA Work Stage* or *OGC Gateway*, the *formal cost plan* for the preceding *RIBA Work Stage* or *OGC Gateway* is to be reviewed by the *employer* and the *project team* to ensure that:

(a)   the building project is affordable;

(b)   the *cost target* for each *element* of the project is reasonable and up to date; and

(c)   the *cost limit* has not been exceeded.

3.5.2   Following the review, the *employer* will sign off the *cost plan* and give any necessary instructions and/or authorise commencement of the next *RIBA Work Stage* or *OGC Gateway*.

3.6 Cost control in procurement

3.6.1   The *cost plan* becomes a fundamental *cost control* mechanism where a building project is procured by the use of separate work packages. By using codified *cost plans*, the *components* allocated to each *element* and *sub-element* can simply be redistributed into the required work packages. Redistributing *components* into work packages will provide *cost targets* for each package, which can be used as a cost management tool during both the *RIBA* Pre-Construction and Construction *Work Stages* and *OGC Gateway* 4 (Readiness for Service).

3.6.2 The method of codifying and redistributing *cost targets* from *elements* to work packages is at paragraph 4.5 of Part 4 of these rules.

3.7 Building projects comprising multiple buildings

3.7.1 Where a building project comprises more than one type of building, it is recommended that a separate *cost plan* be prepared for each building; culminating in a 'summary cost plan' for the entire building project (see Figure 2).

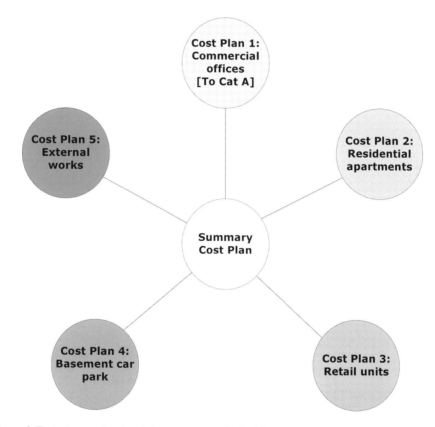

Figure 2: Typical cost plan breakdown structure for building projects comprising multiple buildings

3.8 Information requirements for formal cost plans

3.8.1 The information base of the building project continues to expand during the *RIBA* Design and Pre-Construction *Work Stages* and *OGC Gateways* 3A (Design Brief and Concept Approval), 3B (Detailed Design Approval) and 3C (Investment Decision), as more *project/design team, main contractor*, specialist *subcontractor* and *employer* interaction takes place.

3.8.2 A list of the key information required to enable preparation of *formal cost plans* is at Appendix G of these measurement rules.

3.9 Format, structure and content of elemental cost plans

3.9.1 Examples of templates showing the format, structure and content of *elemental cost plans*, based on level 1 and level 2 code levels, are provided at Appendix H and Appendix I to these rules.

3.10 Measurement rules for building works

3.10.1   The rules of measurement for *building works* (i.e. *group elements* 1 to 9) are detailed in *Part 4: Tabulated rules of measurement for elemental cost planning*.

3.10.2   The degree of detail to be measured for *building work* is to be related to the cost significance of the *elements* in the particular design. Where sufficient information is available, cost significant items are to be measured by means of approximate quantities. Composite items are measured by combining or grouping together work items to common forms of measurement. Non-cost significant items (such as minor items and labours on cost significant items) are ignored in measurement, but are to be accounted for by increasing the applicable *unit rate* by an appropriate percentage or by other appropriate methods.

3.10.3   Quantities shall be given to the nearest whole unit except that any quantity less than one whole unit shall be given as one unit. Quantities measured in tonnes shall be given to two places of decimals.

3.10.4   The method of measuring quantities for each *formal cost plan* shall be as follows:

(a)   **Formal Cost Plan 1**

    (i)   This is the first *formal cost plan*. It coincides with the completion of the concept design at the point where the scope of works is fully defined and key criteria are specified but no detailed design has commenced.

    (ii)   Cost Plan 1 will provide the frame of reference for Cost Plan 2.

    (iii)   The key information required from the *employer* and other *project/design team* members to enable preparation of Formal Cost Plan 1 is set out in Appendix G of these rules.

    (iv)   For Cost Plan 1, a condensed list of *elements* is used, which will be developed into a full list of *elements*, *sub-elements* and *components* as more design and other information becomes available as the building project progresses.

    (v)   Quantities for building works shall be determined in accordance with *Part 4: Tabulated rules of measurement for elemental cost planning* (i.e. *group elements* 1 to 9).

    (vi)   Where insufficient design information is available from which to quantify *building works* in accordance with the rules of measurement for *elemental cost planning*, then the quantity measured is to be the GIFA.

    (vii)   It is likely that a number of alternative concept designs will be considered at this stage.

(b)   **Formal Cost Plan 2**

    (i)   This is the second *formal cost plan*, which coincides with the completion of the design development. Formal Cost Plan 2 is a progression of Formal Cost Plan 1. It is developed by *cost checking* of cost significant *cost targets* for *elements* as more detailed design information is made available from the *design team*.

    (ii)   Cost Plan 2 will provide the frame of reference for Cost Plan 3.

    (iii)   The key information required from the *employer* and other *project/design team* members to enable preparation of Formal Cost Plan 2 is set out in Appendix G of these rules.

    (iv)   The *cost checks* are to be carried out against each pre-established *cost target*.

    (v)   Quantities for *building works* shall be determined in accordance with *Part 4: Tabulated rules of measurement for elemental cost planning* (i.e. *group elements* 1 to 9).

    (vi)   Where insufficient design information is available from which to quantify *building works* in accordance with the rules of measurement for *elemental cost planning*, then the quantity measured is to be the GIFA.

(c)   **Formal Cost Plan 3**

(i)   This third *formal cost plan* stage is based on technical designs, specifications and detailed information for construction. Formal Cost Plan 3 is a progression of Formal Cost Plan 2. It is developed by *cost checking* of cost significant *cost targets* for *elements* as more detailed design information is made available from the *design team*.

(ii)   Cost Plan 3 will provide the frame of reference for appraising tenders.

(iii) The key information required from the *employer* and other *project/design team* members to enable preparation of Formal Cost Plan 3 is set out in Appendix G of these rules.

(iv)   The *cost checks* are to be carried out against each pre-established *cost target*.

(v)   Quantities for building works shall be determined in accordance with *Part 4: Tabulated rules of measurement for elemental cost planning* (i.e. group elements 1 to 9).

(vi)   Where insufficient design information is available from which to quantify *building works* in accordance with the rules of measurement for *elemental cost planning*, then the quantity is measured is to be the GIFA.

3.11   Unit rates used to estimate the cost of building works

3.11.1   The *unit rates* (including *element unit rates* (EUQs) and composite *unit rates*) used to estimate the total cost of *building works* are to include the cost of all materials, labour and plant that are specifically required to construct the item. Costs are also to include any *subcontractors' preliminaries*, design fees, *risk allowances*, and overheads and profit.

3.11.2   *Unit rates* used to estimate the cost of building works (i.e. *building works estimate*) are to exclude *main contractor's preliminaries*, *main contractor's overheads and profit* and other allowances, such as *project/design team fees*, *other development/project costs*, *risk allowances* and *inflation*. These items are to be assessed separately and added to the *building works estimate*.

3.11.3   When using *unit rates* from cost analyses and benchmark analyses, care should be taken to ensure that such rates have been adjusted to reflect prices current at the time the *cost plan* is prepared (i.e. adjusted to remove allowances included for *construction inflation*). Refer to paragraph 2.7.5 at Part 2 of these rules.

3.12   Updating unit rates and other costs to current estimate base date

3.12.1   The *estimate base date* is to be re-established at each *formal cost plan*. Therefore, before using the preceding *order of cost estimate* or *formal cost plan* to progress the next *formal cost plan*, it is essential that the *unit rates* and other rates used in the preceding *order of cost estimate* or *formal cost plan* are updated to bring them into line with the *estimate base date* established for the next *formal cost plan*.

3.12.2   To update a *unit rate* and other rate from the previous *estimate base date* to the current *estimate base date*, the *unit rate* (or other rate) is increased by the amount of inflation occurring during the period from the previous *estimate base date* to the current *estimate base date*. The equation for calculating the updated *unit rate* (or other rate) is therefore:

$$Ra2 = Ra1 + (Ra1 \times p)$$

where:

$Ra1$ = unit rate (or other rate) at previous estimate base date

$Ra2$ = unit rate (or other rate) at current estimate base date p = percentage addition for inflation

The percentage addition for inflation (p) can be computed using published indices (i.e. tender price indices (TPI), building cost indices or retail price indices (RPI)). Alternatively, the percentage addition can be derived from in-house sources of indices. Using published indices, the equation for calculating the percentage addition for *inflation* is therefore:

p = ((index 2 – index 1) ÷ index 1) x 100

where:

index 1 = index at base date of cost data

index 2 = index at current estimate base date

p = percentage addition for inflation

Note: Care should be taken not to update previous rates that were based on percentage additions (e.g. *main contractor's preliminaries, main contractor's overheads and profit* and *project/design team fees*). Such items will be updated when the percentage addition is applied to the updated unit rates (and other rates). Similarly, updating percentages are not to be applied to items for which fixed costs have been agreed (e.g. consultants' fees where based on a fixed lump sum).

3.13 Cost estimate for main contractor's preliminaries

3.13.1 *Main contractor's preliminaries* are a cost significant *element* in most construction projects, which are directly influenced by the choice of construction method more than any other *element*. The *cost checking* of *main contractor's preliminaries* is an iterative process which is repeated at each for each *formal cost plan*.

3.13.2 The methods of estimating the cost of the *preliminaries* will vary according to the *RIBA Work Stage* or *OGC Gateway* reached. To begin with, for Formal Cost Plan 1 (prepared for *RIBA Work Stage* C: Concept or *OGC Gateway* 1: Business Justification), the estimated cost of *main contractor's preliminaries* will be based on a percentage addition derived from a properly considered assessment of cost analyses of previous buildings. However, as more information becomes available a more detailed approach to *cost checking* the *cost target* for *main contractor's preliminaries* is to be taken.

3.13.3 When preparing Formal Cost Plans 2 and 3 (i.e. at *RIBA Work Stages* D, E, and F or at *OGC Gateways* 3A and 3B), to ensure that the previous *cost target* is sufficient, it is essential that thorough *cost checks* are carried out on cost significant items of *main contractor's preliminaries*. To facilitate the *cost checking* process, it is recommended that the checklist of *main contractor's preliminaries* items included in these rules of measurement be used as an aide memoire. (Refer to *Part 4: Tabulated rules of measurement for elemental cost planning*; paragraph 4.2.5).

3.13.4 Where the estimated cost of *main contractor's preliminaries*, or any part of the *main contractor's preliminaries*, is to be based on a percentage addition, the estimated cost is to be calculated by applying the selected percentage addition for *main contractor's preliminaries* to the cost of the *building works estimate*. The equation for calculating the total estimated cost of *main contractor's preliminaries* is therefore:

c = a x b

where:

a = building works estimate (i.e. total estimated cost of building works)

b = percentage for main contractor's preliminaries

c = main contractor's preliminaries estimate (i.e. total estimated cost of main contractor's preliminaries)

3.13.5 Alternatively, the estimated cost of all or part of the *main contractor's preliminaries* can be assessed as a lump sum.

3.13.6 The *main contractor's preliminaries* estimate is added to the *building works estimate*.

3.13.7 Allowance for *subcontractors' preliminaries* is to be made in the *unit rates* applied to measured quantities.

3.13.8 Where the *main contractor* has been appointed early (e.g. as part of a two stage tendering process), the actual agreed level of *main contractor's preliminaries* is to be included in the *cost plan*. Any compensating adjustments are to be made to the applicable *cost targets*.

3.13.9 It is recommended that the allowance for *main contractor's preliminaries* be treated as a separate *cost target*.

3.14 Cost estimate for main contractor's overheads and profit

3.14.1 When preparing a cost estimate for *main contractor's overheads and profit*, overheads and profit can be either combined as a single cost centre or treated as two separate cost centres (i.e. one being *main contractor's overheads* and the other *main contractor's profit*). Main contractor's overheads and profit are to be based on a percentage addition. The estimated cost of any *main contractor's overheads and profit* is to be calculated by applying the selected percentage addition for overheads and profit to the combined total cost of the *building works estimate* and the *main contractor's preliminaries* estimate.

3.14.2 Where *main contractor's overheads and profit* are to be combined as a single cost centre, the equation for calculating the total estimated cost of *main contractor's overheads and profit* is:

$$d = (a + b) \times c$$

where:

a = building works estimate (i.e. total estimated cost of building works)

b = main contractor's preliminaries estimate (i.e. total estimated cost of main contractor's preliminaries)

c = percentage for main contractor's overheads and profit

d = main contractor's overheads and profit estimate (i.e. total estimated cost of main contractor's overheads and profit)

3.14.3 The percentage addition to be applied for combined *main contractor's overheads and profit* is to be derived from a properly considered assessment of *main contractor's overheads and profit* found on previous building projects.

3.14.4 The *main contractor's overheads and profit* estimate is added to the combined total of the *building works estimate* and the *main contractor's preliminaries* estimate. This gives the *works cost estimate*. The equation for calculating the *works cost estimate* is therefore:

$$d = a + b + c$$

where:

a = building works estimate

b = main contractor's preliminaries estimate

c = main contractor's overheads and profit estimate

d = works cost estimate

3.14.5 Where *main contractor's overheads and profit* are to be treated as two separate cost centres, the equations for calculating the total estimated cost of *main contractor's overheads and profit* are as follows:

    (a)   For *main contractor's overheads*:

$$d = (a + b) \times c$$

where:

        a = building works estimate (i.e. total estimated cost of building works)

        b = main contractor's preliminaries estimate (i.e. total estimated cost of main contractor's preliminaries)

        c = percentage for main contractor's overheads

        d = main contractor's overheads estimate (i.e. total estimated cost of main contractor's overheads)

    (b)   For *main contractor's profit*:

$$e = (a + b) \times c$$

where:

        a = building works estimate (i.e. total estimated cost of building works)

        b = main contractor's preliminaries estimate (i.e. total estimated cost of main contractor's preliminaries)

        c = percentage for main contractor's profit

        e = main contractor's profit estimate (i.e. total estimated cost of main contractor's profit)

3.14.6   The percentages addition to be applied for *main contractor's overheads* and *main contractor's profit* are to be derived from a properly considered assessment of *main contractor's overheads and profit* found on previous building projects.

3.14.7   The *main contractor's overheads* and *main contractor's profit* estimates are added to the combined total of the *building works estimate* and the *main contractor's preliminaries* estimate. This gives the *works cost estimate*. The equation for calculating the *works cost estimate* is therefore:

$$e = a + b + c + d$$

where:

        a = building works estimate

        b = main contractor's preliminaries estimate

        c = main contractor's overheads estimate

        d = main contractor's profit estimate

        e = works cost estimate

3.14.8   Where the *main contractor* has been appointed early (e.g. as part of a two-stage tendering process), the actual agreed level of overheads and profit is to be included in the *cost plan*. Any compensating adjustments are to be made to the applicable *cost targets*.

3.14.9   It is recommended that the allowance for *main contractor's overheads and profit* be treated as a separate *cost target*.

3.15 Project/design team fees

3.15.1   *Project/design team fees* are the fees associated with the *project/design team* and other specialist consultants required for the building project (i.e. consultants' fees). *Project/design team fees* also include *main contractor's* pre-construction fees.

3.15.2   A list of typical *project/design team fees* is included in *Part 4: Tabulated rules of measurement for elemental cost planning* (group element 12). The tables are intended to be used by the quantity surveyor/cost manager to assist in the cost estimating and *cost checking* process. The lists are not meant to be definitive or exhaustive, but are merely a guide.

3.15.3   It is recommended that separate allowances be made for:

(a)   consultants' fees;

(b)   *main contractor's* pre-construction fees (if applicable); and

(c)   *main contractor's* design fees (if applicable).

3.15.4   *Project/design team fees* are to be included in *cost plans* unless specifically excluded at the request of the *employer*.

3.15.5   Consultants' fees

(a)   Estimates of consultants' fees are to be based on a percentage addition.

(b)   The estimated cost of consultants' fees is to be calculated by applying the selected percentage addition for consultants' fees to the *works cost estimate* (i.e. the combined total of the *building works estimate*, *main contractor's preliminaries* and *main contractor's overheads and profit*). The equation for calculating *project/design team fees* is therefore:

$$c = a \times b$$

where:

   a = works cost estimate

   b = percentage for consultants' fees

   c = consultants' fees estimate (i.e. total estimated cost of consultants' fees)

(c)   The percentage addition to be applied for *project/design team fees* is to be derived from a properly considered assessment of *project/design team fees* on other similar previous building projects.

(d)   Where actual *project/design team fees* are known (e.g. the architect's fees), the actual fee is to be included in the *cost plan*. Any compensating adjustments are to be made to the applicable *cost targets*.

(e)   Care is to be taken to ensure that the scope of services agreed between the *employer* and a consultant is sufficient to complete the building project when estimating the cost of resources. Any requirement for additional services needs to be identified and allowed for in the *cost plan* (e.g. the cost of carrying out detailed reinforcement design would not normally be included in scope of services (or fee agreement) for the structural engineer, unless specifically requested by the *employer*). Thus, *cost checks* on *project/design team fees* are to include checks on the sufficiency of the scope of services.

(f)   Where a design and build contract strategy has been selected, the responsibility of design will be transferred to the *main contractor*. Therefore, the *design team* members who are to be novated to the *main contractor*, and the timing of the novation, need to be identified. This will enable the *project/design team fees* applicable to those *design team* members to be assessed and redistributed from the *cost target* for consultants' fees to the *cost target* for *main contractor's* design fees as appropriate (see paragraph 3.15.7).

3.15.6   Main contractor's pre-construction fee

(a)   Where it has been decided by the *employer*, in consultation with the *project team*, to employ a *main contractor* (or specialist contractors) to provide pre-construction advice and/or other services, an allowance for the fee for providing such services is to be determined and included in the *cost plan*. The estimated cost of a *main contractor's* pre-construction fees may be calculated by using a percentage addition or derived lump sum.

(b)   Where the estimated cost of the *main contractor's* pre-construction fee is to be based on a percentage, the estimated cost is to be calculated by applying the selected percentage addition for the *main contractor's* pre-construction fee to the *works cost estimate* (i.e. the combined total of the *building works estimate*, *main contractor's preliminaries* and *main contractor's overheads and profit*).

(c)   The percentage addition, or lump sum, to be applied for the *main contractor's* pre-construction fee (or specialist contractor's fees) is to be derived from a properly considered assessment of fees charged on other similar previous building projects; taking account of the type of services required and the duration of the pre-construction period. The equation for calculating the *main contractor's* pre-construction fees is therefore:

$$c = a \times b$$

where:

a = works cost estimate

b = percentage for main contractor's pre-construction fees

c = main contractor's pre-construction fees estimate (i.e. total estimated cost of main contractor's pre-construction fees)

(d)   Care needs to be taken when estimating the cost of pre-construction fees, to ensure that sufficient allowance has been made for *main contractor's overheads and profit* on the pre-construction fee.

3.15.7   Main contractor's design fees

(a)   Where design liability is to be transferred to the *main contractor* (i.e. where a design and build or other *main contractor* led design contract strategy is to be used) and all, or some, of the consultants within the *design team* are to be novated, the balance of the consultants' fees due after novation has occurred are to be transferred from the *cost target* for consultants' fees to the *cost target* for *main contractor's* design fees.

(b)   The allowance for *main contractor's* design fees is to be derived from a properly considered assessment of *main contractor's* design fees found on previous building projects.

3.15.8   The equation for calculating the total *project/design team fees estimate* is therefore:

$$a = F1 + F2 + F3$$

where:

F1 = consultants' fees estimate

F2 = main contractor's pre-construction fees estimate

F3 = main contractor's design fees estimate

a = project/design team fee estimate

3.15.9   The *project/design team fee estimate* is added to the *works cost estimate*.

3.16   Other development/project costs

3.16.1   *Other development/project costs* are for costs that are not necessarily directly associated with the cost of the *building works*, but form part of the total cost of the building project to the *employer* (e.g. insurances, planning fees, fees in connection with party wall awards, decanting and relocation costs, marketing costs and contributions associated with Section 106 Agreements).

3.16.2   *Other development/project costs* are to be included in *cost plans* unless specifically excluded at the request of the *employer*. *Other development/project costs* are to be added as a lump sum allowance.

3.16.3   The nature of *other development/project costs* and the extent of the lump sum allowance to be included in the *cost plan* are to be ascertained in conjunction with the *employer*.

3.16.4   The total estimated cost of *other development/project costs* is added to the combined total of the *works cost estimate* and the *project/design team fees estimate*.

3.16.5   A tabulated list of typical *other development/project costs* is included in *Part 4: Tabulated rules of measurement for elemental cost planning (group element 13)*. The examples provided do not provide a definitive or exhaustive list of items, but are simply a guide.

3.16.6   It is recommended that the allowance for *other development/project costs* be treated as a separate *cost target*.

3.16.7   The combined total of the *works cost estimate*, the *project/design team fees estimate* and the *other development/project costs* estimate is the *base cost estimate*.

3.17 Risk allowances

3.17.1   *Risk allowances*, based on the results of a formal risk analysis, are to be included in each *formal cost plan*. *Risk allowances* are to reflect the *employer's* risk exposure. In setting the amount of the *risk allowances*, the possible consequences of the *employer's residual risk* should be taken into account. The only satisfactory way to ensure that *risk allowances* provide for the risks to the project is to determine the size of the allowances from the results of risk analysis. *Risk allowances* are not to be standard percentages, but a properly considered assessment of the risk, taking account of the completeness of the design and other uncertainties such as the amount of site investigation completed to date.

3.17.2   The need to undertake a formal risk analysis to identify the *employer's* risk exposure and to make considered *risk allowances* for risks is explained in section 2.13 (*risk allowances*) in *Part 2: Measurement rules for order of cost estimating*.

3.17.3   *Risk registers* and risk estimates are to be reassessed at regular intervals throughout the various *RIBA Work Stages* and *OGC Gateways* to ensure that estimates, *formal cost plans* and cash flows realistically reflect the potential impact of any *residual risks*.

3.17.4   Successive assessments are to show decreasing risk due to reducing uncertainty as a consequence of the increasing definition of the project itself and decreasing uncertainty as a result of decisions which are made as the project progresses. However, it should be noted that risk does not always decrease.

3.17.5   It is recommended that *risk allowances* be treated as three separate *cost targets*, which are used to 'top up' other overspending *cost targets* as the project progresses. As an *element* overruns its *cost target*, a transfer is made from the appropriate *risk allowance* to allow for the increase. Similarly, if a *cost target* is likely to under run, the surplus is transferred into the appropriate *risk allowance*. The recommended *cost targets* are:

(a)   design development risks;

(b)   construction risks;

(c)   employer change risks; and

(d)   employer other risks.

Note: See paragraph 2.13.5 (*risk allowances*) in *Part 2: Measurement rules for order of cost estimating* for definitions of the above categories of *risk allowance*.

3.17.6   *Main contractor's* design development risk:

(a)   Where design liability is to be transferred to the *main contractor* (i.e. where a design and build or other *main contractor* led design contract strategy is to be used), it is recommended that an allowance for *main contractor's* design development risk be included in the *risk allowance* for design development risk.

(b)   *Main contractor's* design development risk is a *risk allowance* that the *main contractor* may incorporate in its tender price as the risk of accepting the novation of all, or some, of the *employer's design team* members (e.g. the architect, the structural engineer and the building services engineer).

3.17.7   Where any aspects of *risk allowances* for design development risks, construction risks and *employer* risks are to be based on a percentage addition, the allowances are to be calculated by multiplying the *base cost estimate* by the selected percentage additions. The equations for calculating the *risk allowances* for design development risk, construction risk and *employer* risk are therefore:

for design development risks: $R1 = a \times p1$

for construction risks: $R2 = a \times p2$

for employer change risks: $R3 = a \times p3$

for employer other risks: $R4 = a \times p4$

where:

a = base cost estimate

p1 = percentage risk allowance for design development risks

p2 = percentage risk allowance for construction risks

p3 = percentage risk allowance for employer change risks

p4 = percentage risk allowance for employer other risks

R1 = risk allowance estimate for design development risks (i.e. total estimated cost of risk allowance for design development risks)

R2 = risk allowance estimate for construction risks (i.e. total estimated cost of risk allowance for construction risks)

R3 = risk allowance estimate for employer change risks (i.e. total estimated cost of risk allowance for employer change risks)

R4 = risk allowance estimate for employer other risks (i.e. total estimated cost of risk allowance for employer other risks)

3.17.8　The equation for calculating the total *risk allowance* estimate is therefore:

RA = R1 + R2 + R3 + R4

where:

R1 = risk allowance estimate for design development risks

R2 = risk allowance estimate for construction risks

R3 = risk allowance estimate for employer change risks

R4 = risk allowance estimate for employer other risks

RA = risk allowances estimate

3.17.9　The *risk allowance* estimate is added to the combined total of the *base cost estimate*, *project/design team fee estimate* and the *other development/project costs* estimate. This gives the proposed *cost limit* (excluding *inflation*). The equation for calculating the *cost limit* (excluding *inflation*) is therefore:

CL = a + b

where:

a = base cost estimate

b = risk allowances estimate

CL = cost limit (excluding inflation)

3.17.10　Lists of typical design development risks, construction risks and *employer* risks are included in *Part 4: Tabulated rules of measurement for elemental cost planning (group element* 14: Risks). The lists are intended to be used by the quantity surveyor/cost manager to assist in the cost estimating and *cost checking* process. The lists are not meant to be definitive or exhaustive, but are merely a guide.

3.18 Inflation

3.18.1　*Elemental cost plans* are to be prepared using prices current at the time the estimate is prepared. However, it is also necessary to consider possible future effects of *inflation*. That is price escalation:

(a)　to date of tender (*tender inflation*); and

(b)　during the construction period (*construction inflation*).

3.18.2　For the purpose of *cost planning*, the period used to ascertain the effects of *inflation* are as follows:

(a)　*Tender inflation*: the period from the *estimate base date* to the date of tender return.

(b)   *Construction inflation*: the period from the date of tender return to the mid-point of the construction period.

3.18.3   It is recommended that the allowances for *inflation* be treated as two separate *cost targets* (*tender inflation* and *construction inflation*).

3.18.4   **Tender inflation:** The amount of *tender inflation* is ascertained by applying a single percentage rate for *tender inflation* to the *cost limit* (excluding *inflation*). The addition of *tender inflation* gives the projected *cost limit* (excluding *construction inflation*) for the building project. The equation for calculating the amount of *tender inflation* is therefore:

$$t = CL \times p$$

where:

CL = cost limit (excluding inflation)

p = percentage for tender inflation

t = tender inflation estimate

The percentage for *tender inflation* (p) can be computed using published indices (i.e. tender price indices (TPI), building cost indices or retail price indices (RPI)). Alternatively, the percentage addition can be derived from in-house sources of indices.

Note: This is a simplistic approach to estimating an allowance for *tender inflation*. Where a building project is to be procured by the use of separate works packages, it will be necessary to ascertain a separate allowance for *tender inflation* for each works package; based on the procurement programme for each works package. This is because each works package will be procured at different times throughout the construction period. The method of calculating *tender inflation* for each works package is the same as described above, but with discrete percentages applied to each works package. As part of the *cost control* process, the original allowances for *inflation* will need to be redistributed to each works package from the original cost centre.

3.18.5   The *tender inflation* estimate is added to the *cost limit* (excluding *inflation*). This gives the proposed *cost limit* (excluding *construction inflation*). The equation for calculating the *cost limit* (excluding *construction inflation*) is therefore:

$$CL2 = CL1 + t$$

where:

CL1 = cost limit (excluding inflation)

CL2 = cost limit (excluding construction inflation)

t = tender inflation estimate

3.18.6   **Construction inflation:** The amount of *construction inflation* is ascertained by applying a single percentage rate for *construction inflation* to the *cost limit* (excluding *construction inflation*). The addition of *construction inflation* gives the projected *cost limit* (including *inflation*) for the building project. The equation for calculating the amount of *construction inflation* is therefore:

$$c = CL \times p$$

where:

CL = cost limit (excluding construction inflation)

p = percentage for construction inflation

c = construction inflation estimate

The percentage for *construction inflation* (p) can be computed using published indices (i.e. tender price indices (TPI), building cost indices or retail price indices (RPI)). Alternatively, the percentage addition can be derived from in-house sources of indices.

Notes:

(a) This is a simplistic approach to estimating an allowance for *construction inflation*. Where a building project is to be procured by the use of separate works packages, it will be necessary to ascertain a separate allowance for *construction inflation* for each works package; based on the procurement programme for each works package. This is because each works package will be procured at different times throughout the construction period. The method of calculating *construction inflation* for each works package is the same as described above, but with discrete percentages applied to each works package. As part of the *cost control* process, the original allowances for inflation will need to be redistributed to each works package from the original cost centre.

(b) Care should be taken to ensure that the rates used to calculate an *order of cost estimate* that were derived from cost analyses or benchmark analyses have been adjusted to reflect prices current at the time the *order of cost estimate* is prepared (i.e. adjusted to remove allowances included for *construction inflation*). Refer to paragraph 2.7.5 at Part 2 of these rules.

3.18.7 The construction *inflation* estimate is added to the *cost limit* (excluding *inflation*). This gives the proposed *cost limit* (including *inflation*). The equation for calculating the *cost limit* (including *inflation*) is therefore:

$$CL2 = CL1 + c$$

where:

$CL1$ = cost limit (excluding construction inflation)

$CL2$ = cost limit (including inflation)

c = construction inflation estimate

3.18.8 It is recommended that potential cost increases caused by tendering conditions and the effects of changes in the market are also considered, such as price increases associated with particular materials or products or the impact of major projects sapping resources (home and abroad); or other countries buying major quantities of raw materials (e.g. China). However, it is recommended that such potential cost increases caused by tendering conditions and the effects of changes in the market be dealt with under *risk allowances*.

3.19 Value Added Tax (VAT) assessment

3.19.1 Value Added Tax (VAT) in relation to buildings is a complex area. Therefore, it is recommended that VAT be excluded from *order of cost estimates*.

3.19.2 It is recommended that specialist advice is sought on VAT matters to ensure that the correct rates are applied to the various aspects of a building project.

3.20 Other considerations

3.20.1 Capital allowances for taxation purposes

(a) Capital allowances provide tax relief for certain items of capital expenditure on buildings. This is a valuable form of tax relief that, in most cases, is either under-claimed or not claimed due to the lack of understanding or application of the legislation governing the availability of relief.

(b) Types of allowances include:

- Plant and Machinery Allowance (P&MAs);

- Hotel Building Allowances (HBAs);

- Industrial Building Allowances (IBAs);

- Agricultural Buildings Allowances (ABAs); and

- Research and Development Allowances (R&DAs).

(c)   It is recommended that specialist advice is sought to maximise the availability and quantum of capital allowances.

3.20.2   Land remediation allowances

(a)   Land Remediation Tax Relief provides considerable tax relief for expenditure in remediating contaminated land. Expenditure must be incurred on the prevention, remediation or mitigation of the effects of the pollutant or on the restoration of the land to its former state. The expenditure must be directly linked to the remediation and, as such, general site clearance will not apply.

(b)   It is recommended that specialist advice is sought to maximise the availability and quantum of the tax relief.

3.20.3   Grants

(a)   Grants provide valuable financial aid to funding certain types of building project. These can be significant allowances.

(b)   It is recommended that specialist advice is sought to maximise the availability and quantum of the grants.

3.20.4   Taxation allowances, taxation relief and grants can provide valuable financial aid to an *employer* on certain types of building project. However, it is recommended that specialist advice is sought to maximise the availability and quantum of capital allowances, land remediation relief and grants. For that reason, it is recommended that allowances in connection with capital allowances, land remediation relief and grants be excluded from *cost plans*.

3.21   Reporting of elemental cost plans

3.21.1   Costs are to be expressed as '*cost/m² of GIFA (gross internal floor area)*'.

3.21.2   Where appropriate and/or required by an *employer*, costs may be expressed as a cost/ft² of GIFA or a *cost per functional unit* (or *functional unit cost*) as an alternative to, or in addition to, the *cost/m² of GIFA*. The *functional unit* may be an *employer* defined unit. It is essential, therefore, that the *functional unit* is clearly identified when costs are expressed in this way.

3.21.3   Items included in and excluded from the estimated cost are to be clearly communicated to the *employer* when reporting *cost plans*.

3.21.4   Typical items to be included in *cost plan* reports are as follows:

(a)   project title;

(b)   project description;

(c)   status of *cost plan*;

(d)   a statement of cost (including *cost limit*);

(e)   details of the information and specification on which the *cost plan* was prepared;

(f)   a statement of the floor areas;

(g)   the *cost plan*;

(h)   basis of cost estimates (i.e. assumptions);

(i)   *estimate base date* (i.e. to which *inflation* has been applied);

(j)   reasons for changes to previous *cost targets* (explaining the transfers and adjustments that have taken place against the previous *cost plan*);

(k)   estimated costs of and a request for decisions on any alternative proposals;

(l)   cash flow forecast, where appropriate; and

(m)   inclusions and exclusions (i.e. a statement of what is included in and excluded from the *order of cost estimate*).

Part 4: Tabulated rules of measurement for elemental cost planning

Part 4: Tabulated rules of measurement for elemental cost planning

4.1 Introduction

4.1.1 Part 4 of the rules comprises the rules of measurement for *elemental cost planning*. It explains the use of the tabulated rules and describes how to codifying elemental plans. Advice is also given on how to reallocate costs from *elements* and *sub-elements* to works packages where *building works* are to be procured through the use of works packages.

4.1.2. The rules of measurement for *elemental cost planning* can also be used as a basis for measuring quantities for the application to whole life cycle costing.

4.2 Use of tabulated rules of measurement for elemental cost planning

4.2.1 The rules of measurement for *elemental cost planning* are set out in tables. Tables are provided for each of the following *group elements*:

Group element 1:	Substructure	⎫
Group element 2:	Superstructure	
Group element 3:	Internal finishes	
Group element 4:	Fittings, furnishings and equipment	
Group element 5:	Services	
Group element 6:	Completed buildings and building units	Building works
Group element 7:	Work to existing buildings	
Group element 8:	External works	
Group element 9:	Facilitating works	⎭
Group element 10:	Main contractor's preliminaries	
Group element 11:	Main contractor's overheads and profit	
Group element 12:	Project/design team fees	
Group element 13:	Other development/project costs	
Group element 14:	Risks	
Group element 15:	Inflation	

4.2.2 **Building works:** The tables for *group elements* 1 to 9 comprise the rules of measurement for *building works*. Each table is structured as follows:

(a)   The *group element* is given in the first heading.

(b)   The *element* is given in the second heading.

(c)   The left hand column lists the *sub-elements* and contains the definition rules applicable to each *sub-element*.

(d)   The second and third columns list the *components* and the unit of measurement for *components* respectively.

(e)   The fourth column contains the rules for measuring *components*.

(f)   The next two columns describe the items included and excluded from each *element* and *sub-element*. Where exclusions are stated, cross references to the appropriate *element* or *sub-element* is given.

(g)   Horizontal lines divide the tables to denote the end of a *sub-element*.

(h)   The symbol '/' used between two or more units of measurement in the third column (unit of measurement), means 'or'.

(i)   The rules are written in the present tense.

4.2.3   The tabulated measurement rules are based on four principal levels. Levels 1 to 3 in the rules are headings under which actual work items (i.e. *group element*, *element* and *sub-element*) are allocated. Level 4 are the rules of measurement for *components*.

(a)   **Level 1: *group element***: The primary classifications used for grouping *elements* (i.e. headings).

(b)   **Level 2: *element***: Key part of a *group element*.

(c)   **Level 3: *sub-element***: Part of an *element*. One or more *sub-element* will constitute an *element*.

(d)   **Level 4: *component***: A *building work item* which forms part of a *sub-element*. One or more *components* will be measured to ascertain the cost of an *element* or *sub-element*.

4.2.4   These levels provide the basis of a codified framework for *elemental cost planning*, which can be used both as a frame of reference for *cost checking cost targets* and the overall *cost limit* as more design information becomes available. They provide both a work breakdown structure (*elements*) and a cost breakdown structure (*cost targets*) for a building project.

4.2.5   **Main contractor's preliminaries**: The table for *group element* 10 comprises lists of typical items included in *main contractor's preliminaries*. The table is intended to be used by the quantity surveyor/cost manager to assist in the cost estimating and *cost checking* process. The lists are not meant to be definitive or exhaustive, but are merely a guide. The table is structured as follows:

(a)   The *group element* is given in the first heading.

(b)   The *element* is given in the second heading.

(c)   The *sub-element* is given in the third heading.

(d)   The left hand column lists the *components*.

(e)   The second column decribes the items included in each *element* and *sub-element*. The third column identifies the appropriate unit of measurement for included items. The fourth column describes the excluded items. Where exclusions are stated, cross references to the appropriate *group element*, *element* or *sub-element* are given.

(f)   Horizontal lines divide the tables to denote the end of a *component*.

4.2.6   **Main contractor's overheads and profit**: The table for *group element* 11: Main contractor's overheads and profit is structured as follows:

(a)   The *group element* is given in the first heading.

(b)   The *element* is given in the first column.

(c)   The second and third columns describe the items included and excluded from each *element*. Where exclusions are stated, cross references to the appropriate *element* are given.

(d)   Horizontal lines divide the tables to denote the end of an *element*.

4.2.7   **Project/design team fees**: The table for *group element* 12 comprises lists of typical *project/design team fees*. The table is intended to be used by the quantity surveyor/cost manager to assist in the cost estimating and *cost checking* process. The lists are not meant to be definitive or exhaustive, but are merely a guide. The table is structured as follows:

(a)   The *group element* is given in the first heading.

(b)   The *element* is given in the second heading.

(c)   The left hand column (*component*) comprises a list of typical *project/design team fee* headings.

(d)   The second column describes the items included in each *element* and *sub-element*. The third column identifies the appropriate unit of measurement for included items. The fourth column describes the excluded items. Where exclusions are stated, cross references to the appropriate *element* are given.

(e)   Horizontal lines divide the tables to denote the end of a *component*.

4.2.8   **Other development/project costs**: The table for *group element* 13 comprises a tabulated list of typical *other development/project costs*. The lists are not meant to be definitive or exhaustive, but are merely a guide. The table is structured as follows:

(a)   The *group element* is given in the first heading.

(b)   The *element* is given in the second heading.

(c)   The left hand column (*component*) comprises a list of typical *other development/project cost* headings.

(d)   The second column decribes the items included in each *element* and *sub-element*. The third column identifies the appropriate unit of measurement for included items. The fourth column describes the excluded items. Where exclusions are stated, cross references to the appropriate *element* are given.

(e)   Horizontal lines divide the tables to denote the end of a *component*.

4.2.9   **Risks**: *Group element* 14 comprises lists of typical risks. The lists are not meant to be definitive or exhaustive, but are merely a guide.

(a)   The *group element* is given in the first heading.

(b)   The *element* is given in the second heading.

(c)   The lists set out examples of risk.

4.2.10   **Inflation**: The table for *group element* 15: Inflation is structured as follows:

(a)   The *group element* is given in the first heading.

(b)   The *element* is given in the first column.

(c)   The second and third columns describe the items included and excluded from each *element*. Where exclusions are stated, cross references to the appropriate *element* are given.

(d)   Horizontal lines divide the tables to denote the end of an *element*.

4.3   Work not covered by the rules of measurement for elemental cost planning

4.3.1   Rules of measurement adopted for *components* not covered by the rules of measurement for *elemental cost planning* shall be stated in the *cost plan*. Such rules shall, as far as possible, conform to those rules given in the rules of measurement for similar *components*.

4.4   Method of codifying elemental cost plans

4.4.1   The logic and arrangement of levels for *elemental cost plans* is shown at Appendix F of these rules.

4.4.2   Codes for levels 1 to 3 are provided by the measurement rules, while codes for level 4 (i.e. *components*) will be user defined. This is because of the number of variable *components* that could be generated for any one *sub-element*. It is recommended, therefore, that each *component* measured be numbered sequentially within the *sub-element*. This will allow a unique level 4 code to be established for each *component*. For example:

- Level 1: Superstructure: *group elements* number (2)
- Level 2: Frame: *element* number (1)
- Level 3: Concrete frames: *sub-element* number (4)
- Level 4: Beams (1200mm x 800mm): *component* number (3) – user defined
- Level 4: Beams (2000mm x 800mm): *component* number (4) – user defined

Based on this example, the code for the 1200mm x 800mm beams would be: 3.1.4.3; and the code for the 2000mm x 800mm beams would be: 3.1.4.4.

Further code levels can be added to suit user requirements. For example, a user defined level 5 code can be introduced if there is a need to breakdown the frame into *sub-components*. For example:

- Level 5: Concrete: Number (1)
- Level 5: Formwork: Number (2)
- Level 5: Reinforcement: Number (3)

Based on this example, the code for the reinforcement *sub-component* to the 1200mm x 800mm beams would be: 3.1.4.3.3.

4.4.3   It is essential, therefore, that each *component* be continuously and sequentially numbered under the *sub-element*. Additional code levels can be integrated as necessary to meet other user requirements. This will result in each *component* being given a unique code.

4.5   Method of codifying elemental cost plans for works packages

4.5.1   Where the building project is to be procured through the use of works packages, the works allocated to *elements* and *sub-elements* can be reallocated to the applicable work package. This can be achieved by simply introducing one or more numeric suffix to each item in the *cost plan*. For example:

Work package	Suffix
Main contractor's preliminaries	/001
Substructure and groundworks	/002
Piling	/003
Concrete works (including precast components)	/004
Structural steelwork	/005
Carpentry	/006
Masonry (brickwork and blockwork)	/007
Roof systems and rainwater goods	/008
Joinery (including internal doors, toilet cubicles and vanity units)	/009
Windows and external doors	/010
Curtain walling	/011
Dry linings and partitions	/012
Tiling	/013
Decorating/painting	/014
Floor coverings	/015
Suspended ceilings	/016
Mechanical and electrical services installations (including sanitary appliances)	/017
Lifts	/018
Loose fittings, furnishings and equipment	/019
External drainage	/020
External works – soft landscape works	/021
External works – hard landscape works	/022
Main contractor's overheads and profit	/023

4.5.2   Alternatively, one or more character(s) can be used as a suffix to identify a work package.

4.5.3   If *elements* need to be further broken down, additional levels of code may be introduced to meet user requirements.

Group element I: Substructure

Group element I comprises the following elements:

I.I Foundations

I.2 Basement excavation

I.3 Basement retaining walls

I.4 Ground floor construction

Element I.I: Foundations

Sub-element	Component	Unit	Measurement rules for components	Included	Excluded
I Standard foundations **Definition:** Standard foundations up to and including the damp-proof course.	1 Strip foundations: details, including depth of foundation, to be stated.	m	C1 Where components are to be enumerated, the number of components is to be stated. C2 The linear length of components is measured on the centre line of the component. C3 The volume of disposal of contaminated material measured is the surface area of the contaminated material multiplied by the average depth of the contaminated material. C4 Quantity given for disposal is the bulk before excavating and no allowance is made for subsequent variations to bulk or for extra space to accommodate earthwork support.	1 Wall and column foundations. 2 Foundation walls to underside of damp-proof course (to both perimeter and internal load bearing walls). 3 Isolated pad foundations. 4 Trench and pit excavations, including earthwork support (including insertion and extraction of steel sheet piling if used). 5 Excavating below ground water level. 6 Breaking out surface materials (e.g. hardstandings, pavements and the like). **Note:** Where no information relating to the ground conditions is available, an allowance is to be made within the construction	1 Raft foundations and the like (included in *sub-element* 1.4.1: Ground floor slab/bed and suspended floor construction). 2 Foundations to temporary accommodation (included in *group element* 10: Preliminaries). 3 Forming new contours to the site (included in *sub-element* 8.1.2: Preparatory groundworks). 4 Cultivating and final grading of soil for seeding, turfing or planting (included in *element* 8.3: Planting, as appropriate). 5 Pile caps and ground beams (included in *sub-element* 1.1.2: Piled foundations).
	2 Isolated pad foundations: details, including size of and reinforcement rate (kg/m³) to pile cap, to be stated.	nr			
	3 Extra for disposal of contaminated excavated material: details to be stated.	m³			

Sub-element	Component	Unit	Measurement rules for components	Included	Excluded
			C5 Other cost significant components are to be described and identified separately. Such components are to be measured by area (m²), linear measurement (m) or enumerated (nr) separately in accordance with the rules of measurement for this *sub-element*. C6 Curved work is to be described and identified separately. C7 Work to existing buildings is to be described and identified separately.	*risk allowance* for the extra cost of removing unforeseen obstructions and dealing with unknown ground conditions. 7 Disposal of excavated material, including tipping charges and landfill tax (including inert, non-hazardous and hazardous material where not to be carried out as facilitating works). **Note:** Where no contamination/remediation strategy report exists, an allowance is to be made within the construction *risk allowance* for the extra cost of disposing of contaminated material. 8 Disposal of surface water and ground water, where dewatering techniques not employed. 9 Consolidating and compacting formation level to receive foundations. 10 Blinding. 11 Concrete, reinforcement, formwork (temporary and permanent) and excavating and backfilling of working space required to facilitate placement of formwork. 12 Specialist concrete grades, including waterproof concrete and additives. 13 Brickwork and blockwork walling, including air/ventilation bricks and the like. 14 Forming cavities, including wall ties. 15 Filling cavities. 16 Thermal insulation to cavities. 17 Damp-proof courses. 18 Service ducts and the like through foundation walls. 19 Sundry items. 20 Where works are to be carried out by a *subcontractor, subcontractor's preliminaries*, design fees, risk allowance, overheads and profit.	6 Base slab/bed construction, including damp-proof membranes (included in *sub-element* 1.4.1: Ground floor slab/bed and suspended floor construction). 7 Basement excavation (included in *sub-element* 1.2.1: Basement excavation). 8 Piles (included in *sub-element* 1.1.2: Piled foundations). 9 Basement retaining walls (included in *element* 1.3: Basement retaining walls). 10 Columns (i.e. portion below base slab/bed – included in *element* 2.1: Frame, as appropriate). 11 Drainage (included in *sub-element* 1.4.1: Ground floor slab/bed and suspended floor construction or *sub-element* 8.6.1: Surface water and foul water drainage, as appropriate). 12 Dewatering (included in *sub-element* 9.3.1 Site dewatering and pumping). 13 Soil stabilisation (included in *sub-element* 9.3.2: Soil stabilisation measures). 14 Removing contaminated ground material, where carried out as facilitating works (included in *sub-element* 9.1.2: Contaminated land). 15 Treatment of contaminated ground material, where carried out as facilitating works (included in *sub-element* 9.1.2: Contaminated land).

Sub-element	Component	Unit	Measurement rules for components	Included	Excluded
2 Piled foundations **Definition:** Load bearing foundation piles and caissons.	1 Piling mats/platforms: details, including thickness of mat/platform, to be stated. 2 Piling plant: details to be stated. 3 Moving piling rig to pile position. 4 Piles: details, including type, diameter (mm) and depth (m) of piles, to be stated. 5 Caissons: details, including type, diameter (mm) and depth (m) of caisson, to be stated. 6 Disposal of excavated material arising from piling. 7 Cutting off tops of concrete piles. 8 Pile tests: details to be stated. 9 Vibro-compacted columns: details, including size (mm) and length (m) of column, to be stated. 10 Pile caps: details, including size of and reinforcement rate (kg/m³) to pile cap, to be stated.	m² item nr nr nr m³ item m nr nr	C1 Where components are to be enumerated, the number of components is to be stated. C2 The linear length of components is measured on the centre line of the component. C3 The area measured for piling mats/platforms is the surface area of the piling mat/platform. C4 The volume of disposal of excavated material arising from piling measured is the cross-sectional area of the pile multiplied by the depth of the pile. C5 Quantity given for disposal is the bulk before excavating and no allowance is made for subsequent variations to bulk. C6 Other cost significant components are to be described and identified separately. Such components are to be measured by area (m²), linear measurement (m) or enumerated (nr) separately. C7 Curved work is to be described and identified separately. C8 Work to existing buildings is to be described and identified separately.	1 Piles, including: – precast concrete reinforced piles – precast prestressed concrete piles – precast reinforced segmental concrete piles – bored cast-in-place concrete piles – driven cast-in-place concrete piles – steel bearing piles – timber bearing piles – mini piles. 2 Permanent caissons. 3 Vibro-compacted columns. 4 Piling mats and platforms (installing, moving and removing on completion). 5 Piling rigs/other plant, including bringing to and removing from site, maintenance, erection, dismantling and moving piling rigs to each pile position. **Note:** Where information about ground strata is unknown, an allowance is to be made within the construction *risk allowance* for breaking through obstructions. 6 Ground bearing piles in connection with basement retaining walls. 7 Disposal of excavated material arising from piling, including tipping charges and landfill tax. **Note:** Where no contamination/remediation strategy report exists, an allowance is to be made within the construction *risk allowance* for the extra cost of disposing of contaminated material. 8 Disposal of surface water and ground water, where dewatering techniques not employed. 9 Cutting off excess lengths of piles. 10 Cutting out concrete to tops of piles and preparing pile heads and reinforcement for capping.	1 Piles and caissons forming embedded retaining walls (included in *sub-element* 1.3.2: Embedded basement retaining walls). 2 Dewatering (included in *sub-element* 9.3.1 Site dewatering and pumping). 3 Soil stabilisation (included in *sub-element* 9.3.2: Soil stabilisation measures).

 EFFECTIVE FROM 1 MAY 2009

Sub-element	Component	Unit	Measurement rules for components	Included	Excluded
	11 Ground beams: details, including size of and reinforcement rate (kg/m³) to pile cap, to be stated.	m		11 Grouting.	
				12 Pile tests (e.g. load tests and integrity tests).	
				13 Pile caps.	
				14 Ground beams.	
				15 Trench and pit excavations for pile caps and ground beams, including earthwork support (including insertion and extraction of steel sheet piling if used).	
				16 Disposal of excavated material, including tipping charges and landfill tax. (Refer to Note above about disposal of contaminated material).	
				17 Disposal of surface water and ground water, where dewatering techniques not employed.	
				18 Consolidating and compacting formation level to receive pile caps and ground beams.	
				19 Blinding.	
				20 Protection boarding to underside of pile caps and ground beams (e.g. to provide heave protection).	
				21 Concrete, reinforcement, formwork (temporary and permanent) and excavating and backfilling of working space required to facilitate placement of formwork.	
				22 Specialist concrete grades, including waterproof concrete and additives.	
				23 Sundry items.	
				24 Where works are to be carried out by a subcontractor, subcontractor's preliminaries, design fees, risk allowance, overheads and profit.	

Sub-element	Component	Unit	Measurement rules for components	Included	Excluded
3 Underpinning **Definition:** Inserting additional foundation support under and around existing foundations.	1 Underpinning; details to be stated.	m	C1 The length of underpinning measured is the extreme length. C2 Other cost significant components are to be described and identified separately. Such components are to be measured by area (m²), linear measurement (m) or enumerated (nr) separately in accordance with the rules of measurement for this *sub-element*. C3 Curved work is to be described and identified separately. C4 Work to existing buildings is to be described and identified separately.	1 Underpinning to external walls adjoining the new building. 2 Underpinning to walls within existing buildings, which are to be rehabilitated (i.e. internal walls). 3 Preliminary trenches and underpinning pits, excavation and earthwork support. 4 Temporary supports. 5 Disposal of excavated material, including tipping charges and landfill tax (including inert, non-hazardous and hazardous material where not to be carried out as facilitating works). **Note:** Where no contamination/remediation strategy report exists, an allowance is to be made within the construction *risk allowance* for the extra cost of disposing of contaminated material. 6 Cutting away existing projecting foundations and the like. 7 Preparing existing work to receive pinning up of new work. 8 Concrete, including reinforcement, formwork and additional excavation and backfilling of working space required to facilitate placement of formwork. 9 Masonry (brickwork, blockwork and the like). 10 Waterproof tanking. 11 Sundry items. 12 Where works are to be carried out by a *subcontractor*, *subcontractor's preliminaries*, design fees, risk allowance, overheads and profit.	1 Underpinning to external site boundary walls and the like which are not an integral part of the new building or rehabilitated building (included in *sub-element* 8.8.3: Underpinning to external site boundary walls).

Element 1.2: Basement excavation

Sub-element	Component	Unit	Measurement rules for components	Included	Excluded
1 Basement excavation **Definition:** Bulk excavation required for construction of floors below ground level.	1 Basement excavation: details, including average depth of excavation, to be stated.	m³	C1 The volume measured for Basement excavation and disposal of excavated material is the area of the basement measured to the external face of the external perimeter walls multiplied by the average depth of excavation. C2 The depth of basement excavation shall be measured from either the average existing ground level to the formation level or adjusted ground level (i.e. where a new ground level has been established following preparatory groundworks) to the formation level, whichever is applicable.	1 Bulk excavation to form basements and the like. 2 Temporary or permanent support to the bulk excavation (e.g. earthwork support, caissons, steel sheet piling and the like), including insertion and extraction of temporary steel sheet piling and caissons. 3 Additional excavation required to facilitate construction of basement retaining walls (e.g. where open excavation method is employed), including excavating, back filling (e.g. with selected excavated material or granular material) and disposal of surplus excavated material.	1 Excavation and earthworks to forming new site contours and adjust existing site levels (included in *sub-element* 8.1.2: Preparatory groundworks). 2 Excavation and disposal in connection with trench and pit excavations associated with pile caps, ground beams, retaining walls, ground slabs/beds, raft foundations and drainage below the level from which the basement base slab is to be constructed (included in *sub-element* 1.1.2: Piled foundations, *sub-element* 1.3.1: Basement retaining walls or *sub-element* 1.4.1: Ground floor slab/bed and suspended floor construction, as appropriate). 3 Construction of basement retaining walls (included in *element* 1.3: Basement retaining walls).
	2 Disposal of excavated material: details to be stated.	m³	C3 The volume of disposal of contaminated material measured is the surface area of the contaminated material multiplied by the average depth of the contaminated material. C4 Quantities given for disposal is the bulk before excavating and no allowance is made for subsequent variations to bulk or for extra space to accommodate earthwork support.	4 Excavating below ground water level. 5 Disposal of excavated material, including tipping charges and landfill tax (including inert, non-hazardous and hazardous material where not to be carried out as facilitating works). **Note:** Where no information relating to the ground conditions is available, an allowance is to be made within the construction *risk allowance* for the extra cost of removing unforeseen obstructions and dealing with unknown ground conditions.	4 Excavation and disposal in connection with the construction of diaphragm walling (included in *sub-element* 1.3.2: Embedded basement retaining walls). 5 Construction of base slab/bed (included in *element* 1.4.1: Ground floor slab/bed and suspended floor construction).
	3 Extra for disposal of contaminated excavated material: details to be stated.	m³	C5 The area of earthwork support and working space measured is the full depth to all faces of excavation.	**Note:** Where no contamination/remediation strategy report exists, an allowance is to be made within the construction *risk allowance* for the extra cost of disposing of contaminated material.	6 Excavation and disposal in connection with formation of swimming pools or the like below lowest floor level (included in *sub-element* 1.3.2: Embedded basement retaining walls).
	4 Earthwork support: details to be stated.	m²	C6 Other cost significant components are to be described and identified separately. Such components are to be measured by area (m²), linear measurement (m) or enumerated (nr) separately.	6 Disposal of surface water and ground water, where dewatering techniques not employed. 7 Consolidating and compacting formation level to receive base slab/bed construction. 8 Sundry items.	7 Consolidating and compacting formation level to receive floor construction (included in *element* 1.4: Ground floor construction). 8 Dewatering (included in *sub-element* 9.3.1 Site dewatering and pumping).
	5 Additional excavation: details to be stated.	m²			9 Soil stabilisation (included in *sub-element* 9.3.2: Soil stabilisation measures).

Sub-element	Component	Unit	Measurement rules for components	Included	Excluded
				9 Where works are to be carried out by a *subcontractor, subcontractor's preliminaries,* design fees, risk allowance, overheads and profit.	10 Removing contaminated ground material, where carried out as facilitating works (included in *sub-element 9.1.2:* Contaminated land). 11 Treatment of contaminated ground material, where carried out as facilitating works (included in *sub-element 9.1.2:* Contaminated land).

Element 1.3: Basement retaining walls

Sub-element	Component	Unit	Measurement rules for components	Included	Excluded
1 Basement retaining walls **Definition:** External basement retaining walls in contact with earthwork up to and including the damp-proof course.	1 Basement retaining wall: details to be stated. **Note:** Reinforcement rate (kg/m³) and formwork finish for in-situ concrete walls to be started.	m/m²	C1 Where the length of the basement retaining wall is to be measured, the length of the basement wall shall be measured on the centre line. C2 Where the area of the basement retaining wall is to be measured, the area measured is the surface area of the exposed face of the retaining wall. C3 The height of basement retaining wall shall be measured from the top of the base slab/bed or the top of the basement retaining wall base/toe to the level at which the basement retaining wall connects with the external wall above ground (i.e. at the level at which the external wall changes from being a retaining wall to a non-retaining wall). C4 Where more than one type of retaining wall construction is employed, each type of retaining wall construction is to be stated separately.	1 Concrete retaining walls, including concrete, reinforcement, and formwork and excavating and backfilling working space required to facilitate construction of retaining walls. 2 Specialist concrete grades, such as waterproof concrete. 3 Trench excavations for bases/toes to basement retaining walls which commence below the level from which the construction of the basement base slab is to commence. 4 Disposal of excavated material, including tipping charges and landfill tax (including inert, non-hazardous and hazardous material where not to be carried out as facilitating works). **Note:** Where no contamination/remediation strategy report exists, an allowance is to be made within the construction *risk allowance* for the extra cost of disposing of contaminated material.	1 External basement walls not in contact with earthwork (i.e. non-retaining walls – included in *sub-element 2.5.2:* External walls below ground level). 2 Embedded retaining basement walls – included in *sub-element 1.3.2:* Embedded basement retaining walls). 3 Ground bearing piles in connection with basement retaining walls – included in *sub-element 1.1.2* Piled foundations. 4 Bulk excavation to form basements (included in *sub-element 1.2.1:* Basement excavation). 5 Additional excavation required to facilitate construction of basement retaining walls (e.g. where open excavation method is employed – included in *sub-element 1.2.1:* Basement excavation). 6 Applied finishes to inner faces of external walls (included in *element 3.1:* Wall finishes).

Sub-element	Component	Unit	Measurement rules for components	Included	Excluded
			C5 Other cost significant components are to be described and identified separately. Such components are to be measured by area (m²), linear measurement (m) or enumerated (nr) separately. C6 Curved work is to be described and identified separately.	5 Fixings cast into/fixed to concrete retaining walls to retain masonry walls (e.g. brickwork, blockwork and stonework) facing wall. 6 Masonry walls (e.g. brickwork, blockwork and stonework) forming an integral part of the basement retaining wall construction, including where used for the purpose of concealment (external and internal skins), including reinforcement and design joints. 7 Waterproof tanking to walls. 8 Applied protection to external tanking (e.g. protection boards). 9 Thermal insulation, damp-proof membranes, vapour barriers and the like. 10 Ground water pressure relief drains to basements and retaining walls connected to the drainage system (i.e. fin drains, filter drains and blanket drains). To soil connection. 11 Sundry items associated with the construction of basement retaining walls. 12 Where works are to be carried out by a *subcontractor*, *subcontractor's preliminaries*, design fees, risk allowance, overheads and profit.	7 Retaining walls not providing external walls to building (i.e. which form part of the external works – included in *sub-element* 8.4.3: Retaining walls). 8 Drainage beyond soil connection (included in *sub-element* 1.4.1: Ground floor slab/bed and suspended floor construction or *sub-element* 8.6.1: Surface water and foul water drainage, as appropriate).

Sub-element	Component	Unit	Measurement rules for components	Included	Excluded
2 Embedded basement retaining walls **Definition:** External basement retaining walls consisting of shoulder to shoulder piles or other vertical construction, which are subsequently partially excavated on one side to form retaining walls which obtain their stability from the embedded lower portion.	1 Piling mats/platforms: details, including thickness of mat/platform (mm), to be stated.	m²	C1 Where components are to be enumerated, the number of components is to be stated. C2 The area measured for piling mats/platforms is the surface area of the piling mat/platform.	1 Pile walls (i.e. contiguous bored pile walls; hard/hard secant pile walls; and hard/soft secant pile walls), including guide walls, trimming and cleaning faces, cutting out concrete to tops of piles and preparing pile heads and reinforcement for capping, and disposal of excavated material arising from piling. **Note:** Where no contamination/remediation strategy report exists, an allowance is to be made within the construction risk allowance for the extra cost of disposing of contaminated material.	1 External basement walls not in contact with earthwork, i.e. non-retaining walls (included in sub-element 2.5.2: External walls below ground level). 2 Non-embedded retaining basement walls (included in sub-element 1.3.1: Basement retaining walls). 3 Bulk excavation to form basements (included in sub-element 1.2.1: Basement excavation). 4 Piled walls providing temporary support to excavation works (included in sub-element 1.2.1: Basement excavation). 5 Applied finishes to inner faces of external walls (included in element 3.1: Wall finishes). 6 Retaining walls not providing external walls to building, i.e. which form part of the external works (included in sub-element 8.4.3: Retaining walls). 7 Drainage beyond soil connection (included in sub-element 1.4.1: Ground floor slab/bed and suspended floor construction or sub-element 8.6.1: Surface water and foul water drainage, as appropriate).
	2 Piling plant: details to be stated.	item	C3 Secant piles and the like are to be enumerated.	2 Steel sheet piling, including extensions and cutting off surplus lengths.	
	3 Moving piling rig to pile position.	nr	C4 The linear length of guide walls and contiguous bored pile walls is measured on the centre line of the guide wall or contiguous bored pile wall as applicable.	3 Diaphragm walls, including excavating and disposal of excavated material, support fluid to uphold faces of excavation, concrete, reinforcement, formwork, joints and waterproof joints, guide walls, and trimming and cleaning faces. (Refer to Note above about disposal of contaminated material).	
	4 Guide walls: details to be stated.	m	C5 The area measured for steel sheet piling is the total surface area of specified sheet pile length.	4 Ground anchors.	
	5 Piles: details, including type, diameter (mm), total length (m), exposed length (m) and embedded length (m) of piles, to be stated.	nr	C6 The area measured for diaphragm walls is the area of the diaphragm wall, measured on the centre line of the diaphragm wall. C7 The volume of disposal of excavated material arising from piling measured is the cross-sectional area of the pile multiplied by the depth of the pile.	5 Capping beams, including concrete, reinforcement and formwork. 6 Piling mats and platforms (installing, moving and removing on completion).	
	6 Contiguous bored pile walls: details, including type, diameter (mm), total length (m), exposed length (m) and embedded length (m) of piles, to be stated.	m	C8 Quantity given for disposal is the bulk before excavating and no allowance is made for subsequent variations to bulk. C9 The area measured for trimming and cleaning faces of walls is the surface area of the exposed piled or diaphragm wall. C10 The linear length of capping beams is measured on the centre line of the capping beam.	7 Pile rigs/other plant, including bringing to and removing from site, maintenance, erection, dismantling and moving piling rigs to each pile position.	
	7 Disposal of excavated material arising from piling.	m³	C11 The area measured for each basement component is the area of the component. The area measured is the surface area of the component, measured on the centre line of the component.	8 Pile tests (e.g. load tests and integrity tests). 9 Instrumentation and monitoring.	
	8 Cutting off tops of concrete piles.	nr/m		10 Groundwater pressure relief drains to basements and retaining walls connected to the drainage system (i.e. fin drains, filter drains and blanket drains). To soil connection.	

Sub-element	Component	Unit	Measurement rules for components	Included	Excluded
	9 Steel sheet piling: details, including total area (m²) and total driven area (m²) to be stated.	m²	C12 The area measured for concrete applied by spray or gun is the surface area of the surface to which it is to be applied.	11 Concrete walls forming an integral part of the embedded basement wall construction, including reinforcement, tying to piled wall formwork.	
	10 Cutting off surplus lengths steel sheet piling.	nr	C13 Other cost significant components are to be described and identified separately. Such components are to be measured by area (m²), linear measurement (m) or enumerated (nr) separately.	12 Specialist concrete grades, such as waterproof concrete.	
	11 Pile tests: details to be stated.	item	C14 Curved work is to be described and identified separately.	13 Temporary works (e.g. props and wallings to support contiguous bored pile walls).	
	12 Diaphragm walls: details, including depth of excavation, thickness (mm) of wall reinforcement rate (kg/m³), to be stated.	m²		14 Fixings cast into/fixed to concrete retaining walls to retain masonry walls (e.g. brickwork, blockwork and stonework) facing wall.	
	13 Ground anchors: details, including type, to be stated.	nr		15 Masonry walls/facings (e.g. brickwork, blockwork and stonework) forming an integral part of the embedded basement retaining wall.	
	14 Trimming and cleaning faces of piled and diaphragm walls.	m²		16 Waterproof tanking to walls.	
	15 Temporary works: details to be stated.	item		17 Applied protection to external tanking (e.g. protection boards).	
	16 Capping beams: details, including beam size (mm) and reinforcement rate (kg/m³), to be stated.	m		18 Thermal insulation, damp-proof membranes, vapour barriers and the like.	
	17 Basement retaining wall components: details to be stated. Note: Reinforcement rate (kg/m³) and formwork finish for in-situ concrete walls to be stated.	m²		19 Concrete applied by spray or gun, including reinforcement, formwork and design joints.	
				20 Sundry items.	
				21 Where works are to be carried out by a subcontractor, subcontractor's preliminaries, design fees, risk allowance, overheads and profit.	

Sub-element	Component	Unit	Measurement rules for components	Included	Excluded
	18 Concrete applied by spray or gun: details, including thickness (mm), to be stated.	m²			

Element 1.4: Ground floor construction

Sub-element	Component	Unit	Measurement rules for components	Included	Excluded
1 Ground floor slab/bed and suspended floor construction **Definition:** The entire lowest floor assembly below the underside of screed or lowest floor finish.	1 Lowest floor construction: details to be stated. **Note:** Reinforcement rate (kg/m³ or kg/m² as appropriate) for concrete slabs and beds to be stated. 3 Extra over lowest floor construction for forming ramps and the like: details to be stated. 4 Extra over lowest floor construction for forming of lift pits and the like: details, including the number and size of lift pits, to be stated.	m² m² nr	C1 The area measured is the area of the floor construction measured to the internal face of the external perimeter walls. C2 The area of the floor construction shall be measured in accordance with the rules of measurement for ascertaining the gross internal floor area (GIFA). C3 Where more than one type of floor construction is employed, the area measured for each floor construction is the area covered by that floor construction. C4 The length of retaining walls at changes in level measured is their extreme length, over all obstructions. The height measured is the distance from top of the slab to the underside of the attached slab. C5 The area measured for forming swimming pool tanks and the like is the area of the swimming pool (or other similar facility) on plan, measured to the internal face of the swimming pool walls. C6 The area measured for forming lift pits and the like is the area of the lift pit on plan, measured to the internal face of the lift pit. C7 The length of linear components measured is their extreme length, over all obstructions.	1 Lowest floor assemblies, such as: – ground slabs/beds – basement slabs/beds – raft foundations – suspended floors serving as lowest floor level systems, i.e. where void between ground slab/bed under and lowest floor slab (including, suspended timber floor construction and precast/composite decking systems). 2 Thickening to slabs/beds for load-bearing walls, machine bases and the like. 3 Inclined and stepped slabs/beds. 4 Ramps in slabs 5 Retaining walls at changes in level. 6 Lift pits and the like below the lowest floor: Including waterproofing. 7 Swimming pool tanks, including boom pits, and the like. Including waterproofing. 8 Surface area excavations (i.e. to remove top soil and to reduce levels), including earthwork support. 9 Pit excavations, including earthwork support. 10 Disposal of excavated material, including tipping charges and landfill tax (including inert,	1 Bulk excavation to form basements (included in *sub-element* 1.2.1: Basement excavation). 2 Non-structural screeds (included in *sub-element* 3.2.1: Finishes to floors). 3 Floating floors (included in *sub-element* 3.2.1: Finishes to floors). 4 Applied floor finishes (included in *sub-element* 3.2.1: Finishes to floors). 5 Finishes to swimming pool tanks, including tank linings (included in *sub-element* 3.2.1: Finishes to floors). 6 Hardeners and sealers applied to slabs/beds after construction (included in *sub-element* 3.2.1: Finishes to floors). 7 Podium slabs, transfer slabs and other suspended upper floor constructions forming part of the basement construction (included in *element* 2.2: Upper floors). 8 Basement roofs, i.e. where not performing as a floor (included in *element* 2.3: Roof). 9 Machine bases constructed on top of slabs and beds (included in *element* 5.14: Builder's work in connection with services).

Sub-element	Component	Unit	Measurement rules for components	Included	Excluded
	5 Extra over lowest floor construction for forming swimming pool tanks and the like: details, including the size, to be stated.	nr	C8 The length of below ground drainage pipelines measured is their extreme length, over all fittings, branches and the like. C9 Where components are to be enumerated, the number of components is to be stated. C10 Other cost significant components are to be described and identified separately. Such components are to be measured by area (m²), linear measurement (m) or enumerated (nr) separately. C11 Curved work is to be described and identified separately. C12 Work to existing buildings is to be described and identified separately.	non-hazardous and hazardous material where not to be carried out as facilitating works). **Note:** Where no contamination/remediation strategy report exists, an allowance is to be made within the construction *risk allowance* for the extra cost of disposing of contaminated material. 11 Disposal of surface water and ground water, where dewatering techniques not employed. 12 Consolidating and compacting formation level to receive floor construction. 13 Concrete, reinforcement, formwork (temporary and permanent), and working space for formwork. 14 Specialist concrete grades, such as waterproof concrete. 15 Filling to make up levels. 16 Blinding beds. 17 Protection boarding to underside of floor/base slabs (e.g. to provide heave protection). 18 Damp-proof membranes, including gas proof membranes serving as a damp-proof membrane. 19 Service ducts and the like below the lowest floor construction. 20 Fixing devices cast into concrete (i.e. dowels, anchor bolts, anchor boxes, anchor fixing slots and the like). 21 Design joints, including at intersection of base slab/bed and external perimeter wall, to provide bays and the like. 22 Worked finishes (i.e. in-situ surface treatments), including the application of surface hardeners and power floated finishes. 23 Structural screeds, including reinforcement.	10 Drainage beyond the first manhole external to the enclosing walls of the building (included in *sub-element* 8.6.1: Surface water and foul water drainage). 11 Ground gas venting to the entire site (included in *sub-element* 9.3.3: Ground gas venting measures, as appropriate).
	6 Retaining walls at changes in level: details, including thickness (mm), height (m) and reinforcement rate (kg/m³), to be stated.	m			
	7 Designed joints: details, including height (mm), to be stated.	m			
	8 Drainage below ground: details, including average depth of trench (m), type and nominal size of pipe (mm), and materials for beds and haunchings/surrounds, to be stated.	m			
	9 Gullies, floor outlets and the like: details to be stated.	nr			
	10 Internal manholes, catch-pits, petrol interceptors or the like: details to be stated.	nr			

Sub-element	Component	Unit	Measurement rules for components	Included	Excluded
				24 Suspended timber floors, including floor boards, joists, joist struts, plates and the like. Including supporting masonry/concrete walls under (i.e. load-bearing sleeper walls).	
				25 Precast/composite decking systems, including concrete components, in-situ concrete, site fixed formwork and reinforcement, filler units, fixing slips, metal clips and other fixings, joints (including grouting joints), worked finishes and performance tests.	
				26 Drainage below or within lowest floor assembly, including pipework, pipework ancillaries (e.g. gullies, gratings, rodding and access points) and fittings to pipework (to first manhole beyond the external enclosing walls).	
				27 Internal manholes and the like, including channels benching, step irons, access covers and other accessories.	
				28 Floor outlets.	
				29 Prefabricated floor channels and gratings in ground floor construction.	
				30 Trenches for pipework, including excavation, earthwork support, backfilling and disposal of surplus material.	
				31 Granular beds and surround, concrete beds, cradles, haunching and surrounds, and foamed concrete backfill.	
				32 Venting below building (e.g. radon sumps under ground slab/bed).	
				33 Special filling material beneath base slab/bed.	
				34 Sundry items.	
				35 Where works are to be carried out by a subcontractor, subcontractor's preliminaries, design fees, risk allowance, overheads and profit.	

Group element 2: Superstructure

Group element 2 comprises the following elements:

2.1 Frame

2.2 Upper floors

2.3 Roof

2.4 Stairs and ramps

2.5 External walls

2.6 Windows and external doors

2.7 Internal walls and partitions

2.8 Internal doors

Element 2.1: Frame

Sub-element	Component	Unit	Measurement rules for components	Included	Excluded
1 Steel frames **Definition:** Structural steelwork in frames, including all components, fittings, fixings and components.	1 Structural steel frame, including fittings and fixings: details, including size of column grid (m), to be stated. 2 Fire protection to steel frame: details to be stated. 3 Factory applied paint systems: details to be stated.	t t t	C1 The total mass of the steel frame is to be stated. The mass of framing includes all fittings and components. C2 The mass measured for fire protection and paint system is the total mass of the structural steel frame. C3 Work to existing buildings is to be described and identified separately.	1 Structural steel frame, including all components (e.g. columns, beams, composite columns and beams, lattice beams, braces, struts and the like). 2 Fittings and fixings. 3 Roof trusses, where an integral part of the frame and cannot be separated from the frame. 4 Floor and roof members or decks forming an integral part of the frame, which cannot be separated from the frame.	1 Space frames and decks, including structural support framework (included in *sub-element* 2.1.2: Space frames/decks). 2 Specialist, proprietary and modular lightweight steel frame systems (included in *sub-element* 2.1.5: Specialist frames). 3 Roof trusses which can be separated from the frame (included in *sub-element* 2.3.1: Roof structure).

Sub-element	Component	Unit	Measurement rules for components	Included	Excluded
				5 Fabrication, trial erection and permanent erection on site (including holding down bolts, assemblies, grouting under base plates and the like). 6 Factory applied coatings, including fire protective coatings and paint systems. 7 Sundry items. 8 Where works are to be carried out by a subcontractor, subcontractor's preliminaries, design fees, risk allowance, overheads and profit.	4 Floor, roof and wall structures which can be separated from the frame (included in sub-element 2.3.1: Roof structure; element 2.5: External walls or element 2.7: Internal walls and partitions as appropriate). 5 Beams forming an integral part of a floor or roof which can be separated from the frame (included in element 2.2: Upper floors or sub-element 2.3.1: Roof structures as appropriate). 6 Lintels (included in element 2.6: Windows and external doors or element 2.8: Internal doors as appropriate). 7 Casing steel members in concrete for protection (included in sub-element 2.1.3: Concrete casings to steel frames). 8 Site applied decorative painting additional to factory applied protection and paint systems (included in group element 3: Internal finishes, as appropriate).
2 Space frames/decks **Definition:** Space frames/decks, including structural support framework, and including all components.	1 Space frame/deck, including structural support framework, fittings and fixings: details to be stated. 2 Fire protection to steel frame: details to be stated. 3 Factory applied paint systems: details to be stated.	m² m² m²	C1 The area measured is the area of the upper floors. The area is measured using the rules of measurement for ascertaining the gross internal floor area (GIFA).	1 Space frames/decks, including fittings and fixings. 2 Structural support framework. 3 Fittings and fixings. 4 Fabrication, trial erection and permanent erection on site (including holding down bolts, assemblies, grouting under base plates and the like). 5 Factory applied coatings, including fire protective coatings and paint systems. 6 Sundry items. 7 Where works are to be carried out by a subcontractor, subcontractor's preliminaries, design fees, risk allowance, overheads and profit.	1 Casing steel members in concrete for protection (included in sub-element 2.1.3: Concrete casings to steel frames). 2 Site applied decorative painting additional to factory applied protection and paint systems (included in group element 3: Internal finishes).

Sub-element	Component	Unit	Measurement rules for components	Included	Excluded
3 Concrete casings to steel frames **Definition:** Protective casings to columns and beams for structural or protective purposes, including fire protection.	1 Column casings: details, including number of columns (nr), column size and type of formwork finish, to be stated. 2 Beam casings: details, including number of beams (nr), beam size and type of formwork finish, to be stated.	m m	C1 Where components are to be enumerated, the number of components is to be stated. C2 Column casings: The linear length measured is the distance between the top of the slab/bed, pile cap or ground beam (as appropriate) and the soffit of the beam attached to the next floor level (or to soffit of suspended slab if no beams). C3 Beam casings: The linear length is measured on the centre line of the beam. C4 No deduction is made for volume of steel. C5 Concrete additives: details to be stated. C6 Complex shapes: details to be stated. C7 Special formed finishes: details to be stated. C8 Work to existing buildings is to be described and identified separately.	1 Concrete. 2 Specialist concrete grades and additives. 3 Formwork. 4 Special formed finishes to in-situ concrete. 5 Sundry items. 6 Where works are to be carried out by a *subcontractor*, *subcontractor's preliminaries*, design fees, risk allowance, overheads and profit.	
4 Concrete frames **Definition:** Concrete columns and beams.	1 Columns: details, including number (nr) of columns, column size (mm), concrete grade, reinforcement rate (kg/m³) and type of formwork finish, to be stated. 2 Beams details, including number (nr) of beams, beam size (mm), reinforcement rate (kg/m³) and type of formwork finish, to be stated.	m m	C1 Columns: The linear length measured is the distance between the top of the slab/bed, pile cap or ground beam (as appropriate) and the soffit of the beam attached to the next floor level (or to soffit of suspended slab if no beams). C2 Size of column grid to be stated. C3 Beams: the linear length is measured on the centre line of the beam. **Notes:** (1) Where upper floors do not form an integral part of the structural frame, the beam size stated is the total width by the total depth.	1 Beams. 2 Columns, blade columns and the like. 3 Walls and core walls forming an integral part of the structural assembly. 4 Concrete. 5 Specialist concrete grades and additives. 6 Reinforcement, including starter bars, punching shear reinforcement and the like. 7 Reinforcement for precast, prestressed and post-tensioned concrete, including stressing cables, applying stressing and the like. 8 Formwork. 9 Designed joints (e.g. to walls). 10 Worked finishes (i.e. in-situ surface treatments), including the application of surface hardeners.	1 Upper floors (included in *element 2.2*: Upper floors). 2 Roof slabs (included in *sub-element 2.3.1*: Roof structure).

Sub-element	Component	Unit	Measurement rules for components	Included	Excluded
	3 Walls: details, including thickness of wall (mm), concrete grade, reinforcement rate (kg/m³) and type of formwork finish, to be stated.	m²	(2) Where upper floors form an integral part of the structural frame, the beam size stated is the total width by the depth below the concrete floor (measured from the underside of the concrete floor to the bottom/underside of the beam). Notwithstanding this, an appropriate allowance shall be made in the unit rate for beam reinforcement that is integrated within the concrete floor).	11 Special formed finishes to in-situ concrete. 12 Grouting up of frame components. 13 Forming openings for doors, windows, screens and the like. 14 Sundry items. 15 Where works are to be carried out by a subcontractor, subcontractor's preliminaries, design fees, risk allowance, overheads and profit.	
	4 Extra over walls for forming openings in walls for doors, windows, screens and the like: details, including thickness of wall (mm), overall size of opening (m) and type of formwork finish, to be stated.	nr	C4 Walls: the area measured is the area of the wall, measured on the centre line of the wall. No deduction is made for door openings, windows, screens and the like. C5 No deduction is made for volume of steel. C6 Concrete grade/mix to be stated. C7 Concrete additives: details to be stated. C8 Complex shapes: details to be stated. C9 Special formed finishes: details to be stated. C10 Curved work is to be described and identified separately.		
	5 Designed joints: details to be stated.	m	C11 Work to existing buildings is to be described and identified separately.		

Sub-element	Component	Unit	Measurement rules for components	Included	Excluded
5 Timber frames **Definition:** Timber frame systems, including all components.	1 Timber frames: details to be stated.	m²	C1 The area measured is the area of the upper floors. The area is measured using the rules of measurement for ascertaining the gross internal floor area (GIFA). C2 Area measured to include area of roof, where roof structure (including roof trusses) is an integral part of the frame. C3 Details of floor, roof (including trussed roofs) and wall members or decks which cannot be separated from the frame are to be stated.	1 Complete timber frame systems, including all components and fixings. 2 Panel system such as off-site manufactured timber frames. 3 Laminated timber structures and the like. 4 Roof trusses, where an integral part of the frame and cannot be separated from the frame. 5 Floor, roof and structural wall members, including wall linings and floor boarding, forming an integral part of the frame, which cannot be separated from the frame system. 6 Specialist *subcontractor/supplier* design of timber frame. 7 Trial erection and permanent erection on site of timber frame (when required). 8 Treatments to timber. 9 Site applied fire retarding paint. 10 Sundry items. 11 Where works are to be carried out by a *subcontractor, subcontractor's preliminaries,* design fees, risk allowance, overheads and profit.	1 Prefabricated complete and semi-complete buildings and modular room units (included in *element 6.1:* Prefabricated buildings). 2 Roof trusses which can be separated from the frame (included in *sub-element 2.3.1:* Roof structure). 3 Floor, roof and structural wall members, including wall linings and floor boarding, which can be separated from the frame (included in *sub-element 2.2.3:* Timber floors; *sub-element 2.3.1:* Roof structure; *element 2.5:* External walls or *element 2.7:* Internal walls and partitions, as appropriate). 4 Finishes applied to external walls and internal walls, floors and ceilings (included in *sub-element 2.5.1:* External walls above ground level, *sub-element 2.5.2:* External walls below ground level or *group element 3:* Internal finishes, as appropriate).

Sub-element	Component	Unit	Measurement rules for components	Included	Excluded
6 Specialist frames **Definition:** Specialist structural frame systems, including all components.	1 Specialist frame: details to be stated.	m²	C1 The area measured is the area of the upper floors. The area is measured using the rules of measurement for ascertaining the gross internal floor area (GIFA).	1 Portal frames and similar individual structural units (steel, concrete, timber or other material). 2 Specialist, proprietary and modular lightweight steel frame systems. 3 Cellular construction such as tunnel (slip) form. 4 Components, fittings and fixings. 5 Roof trusses, where an integral part of the frame and cannot be separated from the frame. 6 Floor and roof members or decks forming an integral part of the frame, which cannot be separated from the frame. 7 Fabrication, trial erection and permanent erection on site (including holding down bolts, assemblies, grouting under base plates and the like). 8 Factory applied coatings, including fire protective coatings and paint systems. 9 Sundry items. 10 Where works are to be carried out by a subcontractor, subcontractor's preliminaries, design fees, risk allowance, overheads and profit.	1 Structural steel frames (included in sub-element 2.1.1: Steel frames/decks). 2 Space frames and decks (included in sub-element 2.1.2: Space frames). 3 Concrete frames (included in sub-element 2.1.4: Concrete frames). 4 Timber frames (included in sub-element 2.1.5: Timber frames). 5 Prefabricated buildings and structures (included in group element 6: Complete buildings and building units). 6 Floor, roof and structural wall members, including wall linings and floor boarding which can be separated from the frame (included in sub-element 2.2.3: Timber floors; sub-element 2.3.1: Roof structure; element 2.5: External walls or element 2.7: Internal walls and partitions, as appropriate).

Element 2.2: Upper floors

Sub-element	Component	Unit	Measurement rules for components	Included	Excluded
1 Concrete floors **Definition:** Reinforced and post tensioned concrete suspended floors.	1 Suspended floor slabs: details, including thickness (mm); concrete strength (N/mm²), reinforcement rate (kg/m³) and type of formwork finish, to be stated.	m²	C1 The area measured is the area of the upper floors. The area is measured using the rules of measurement for ascertaining the gross internal floor area (GIFA). No deduction is to be made for beams which form an integral part of the upper floor. C2 Where more than one floor construction type is employed, the area measured for each floor construction type is measured.	1 Concrete suspended floors, including: – upper floors – podium slabs forming roofs to basements – transfer structures – balconies (internal and external) which are an integral part of the suspended floor construction – mezzanine floors	1 Basement roofs, i.e. where not acting as a podium slab or transfer slab (included in *element* 2.3: Roof). 2 Non-structural screeds (included in *sub-element* 3.2.1: Finishes to floors). 3 Structural screeds (included in *sub-element* 2.2.4: Structural screeds). 4 Floating floors (included in *sub-element* 3.2.1: Finishes to floors).
	2 Edge formwork: details of formwork finish to be stated.	m	C3 Where more than one floor construction type is employed, the combined area of each floor construction type shall equal the total area of the upper floors.	– service floors and the like – galleries, tiered terraces and the like – walkways, internal bridges and the like – external corridors/bridges forming links between buildings, including supporting frames	5 Applied floor finishes (included in *sub-element* 3.2.1: Finishes to floors). 6 Hardeners and sealers applied to suspended floor slabs after construction (included in *element* 3.2.1: Finishes to floors). 7 Raised access floors (included in *sub-element* 3.2.2: Raised access floors).
	3 Designed joints: details to be stated.	m	C4 Areas for balconies, galleries, tiered terraces, service floors, walkways, internal bridges, external links, roofs to internal buildings, shall be shown separately. C5 Sloping surfaces to be measured flat on plan.	– beams which form an integral part of the floor in framed buildings – floor beams in unframed building – roofs to internal buildings, where an integral part of the upper floor construction.	8 Applied ceiling finishes (included in *sub-element* 3.3.1: Finishes to ceilings). 9 False ceilings (included in *sub-element* 3.3.2: False ceilings). 10 Suspended ceilings (included in *sub-element* 3.3.3: Demountable suspended ceilings).
	4 Surface treatments: details to be stated.	m²	**Note:** Where balconies are included, the area of the upper ground floor and lowest ground floor will exceed the GIFA. C6 The length of linear components measured is their extreme length. Curved work is to be described and identified separately. C7 Work to existing buildings is to be described and identified separately.	2 Reinforced concrete floors, including solid, waffle and trough slabs. Including all concrete, reinforcement (including punching shear reinforcement) and formwork (to soffits, edges and openings). 3 Post tensioned concrete floors, including concrete, reinforcement, (i.e. stressing cables), formwork, applying stressing and grouting up) and formwork.	11 Roofs to internal buildings which are not an integral part of the upper floor construction, floor area (included in *element* 2.3: Roof). 12 Structural screeds applied to roof decking (included in *sub-element* 2.3.1: Roof structure).

Sub-element	Component	Unit	Measurement rules for components	Included	Excluded
				4 Worked finishes (i.e. in-situ surface treatments), including tamped finish, power float finish the application of surface hardeners. 5 Permanent formwork, including profiled sheet metal decking. 6 Designed joints. 7 Sundry items. 8 Where works are to be carried out by a *subcontractor, subcontractor's preliminaries,* design fees, risk allowance, overheads and profit.	13 Balconies which are not an integral part of the upper floor construction (included in *sub-element* 2.2.5: Balconies). 14 Drainage to balconies which are an integral part of the upper floor construction (included in *sub-element* 2.2.6: Drainage to balconies).
2 Precast/composite decking systems **Definition:** Floor decks consisting of proprietary precast units, a combination of in-situ concrete with filler units of other material.	1 Suspended floor slab: details, including type, thickness (mm); span (m) and loading (kN/m²), to be stated.	m²	C1 The area measured is the area of the upper floors. The area is measured using the rules of measurement for ascertaining the gross internal floor area (GIFA). C2 Where more than one floor construction type is employed, the area measured for each floor construction type is measured. C3 Where more than one floor construction type is employed, the combined area of each floor construction type shall equal the total area of the upper floors. C4 Areas for balconies, galleries, tiered terraces, walkways, internal bridges, external links, and roofs to internal buildings shall be shown separately. C5 Sloping surfaces to be measured flat on plan. **Note:** Where balconies are included, the area of the upper ground floor and lowest ground floor will exceed the GIFA. C6 Work to existing buildings is to be described and identified separately.	1 Suspended floors, including: – upper floors – podium slabs forming roofs to basements – balconies (internal and external) which are an integral part of the suspended floor construction – mezzanine floors – service floors and the like – galleries, tiered terraces and the like – walkways, internal bridges and the like – external corridors/bridges forming links between buildings, including supporting frames – roofs to internal buildings, where an integral part of the upper floor construction. 2 Solid, hollow, tee or other section precast and prestressed concrete plank and slab decks. 3 Composite decks of precast and prestressed concrete beams with filler blocks of precast concrete, in-situ concrete and other materials.	1 Precast/composite decking systems used in ground floor construction (included in *sub-element* 1.4.1: Ground floor slab/bed and suspended floor construction). 2 Precast decking forming an integral part of precast concrete frame assemblies (included in *sub-element* 2.1.6: Specialist frames). 3 Basement roofs, i.e. where not acting as a podium slab or transfer slab (included in *element* 2.3: Roof). 4 Non-structural screeds (included in *element* 3.2: Floor finishes). 5 Structural screeds (included in *sub-element* 2.2.4: Structural screeds or *sub-element* 2.3.1: Roof structure, as appropriate). 6 Hardeners and sealers applied to suspended floor slabs after construction (included in *element* 3.2.1: Finishes to floors). 7 Floating floors (included in *sub-element* 3.2.1: Finishes to floors). 8 Applied floor finishes (included in *sub-element* 3.2.1: Finishes to floors).

Sub-element	Component	Unit	Measurement rules for components	Included	Excluded
				4 Composite decks of in-situ concrete on precast or prestressed concrete planks. 5 Hollow tile decks of in-situ concrete with filler blocks of clay, precast concrete or other material. 6 Precast and prestressed concrete components. 7 In-situ concrete. 8 Site fixed formwork and reinforcement. 9 Filler units. 10 Fixing slips, metal clips and other fixings. 11 Joints, including grouting joints. 12 Worked finishes (i.e. in-situ surface treatments), including the application of surface hardeners. 13 Performance tests. 14 Sundry items. 15 Where works are to be carried out by a subcontractor, subcontractor's preliminaries, design fees, risk allowance, overheads and profit.	9 Raised access floors (included in sub-element 3.2.2: Raised access floors). 10 Applied ceiling finishes (included in sub-element 3.3.1: Finishes to ceilings). 11 False ceilings (included in sub-element 3.3.2: False ceilings). 12 Suspended ceilings (included in sub-element 3.3.3: Demountable suspended ceilings). 13 Roofs to internal buildings which are not an integral part of the upper floor construction (included in sub-element 3.3.3: Demountable suspended ceilings). 14 Balconies which are not an integral part of the upper floor construction (included in sub-element 2.2.5: Balconies). 15 Drainage to balconies which are an integral part of the upper floor construction (included in sub-element 2.2.6: Drainage to balconies).

Sub-element	Component	Unit	Measurement rules for components	Included	Excluded
3 Timber floors **Definition:** Structural timber floor construction, including floor boards.	1 Timber floors: details to be stated.	m²	C1 The area measured is the area of the upper floors. The area is measured using the rules of measurement for ascertaining the gross internal floor area (GIFA). C2 Where more than one floor construction type is employed, the area measured for each floor construction type is measured. C3 Where more than one floor construction type is employed, the combined area of each floor construction type shall equal the total area of the upper floors. C4 Areas for balconies, galleries, tiered terraces, walkways, internal bridges, external links, and roofs to internal buildings shall be shown separately. C5 Sloping surfaces to be measured flat on plan. **Note:** Where balconies are included, the area of the upper ground floor and lowest ground floor will exceed the GIFA. C6 Work to existing buildings is to be described and identified separately.	1 Timber suspended floors, including: – upper floors – balconies (internal and external) which are an integral part of the suspended floor construction – mezzanine floors – service floors and the like – galleries, tiered terraces and the like – walkways, internal bridges and the like – external corridors/bridges forming links between buildings, including supporting frames – roofs to internal buildings, where an integral part of the upper floor construction. 2 Structural floor members, including joists, struts, trimmers, plates and the like. 3 Carpenter's metalwork, including strutting, joist hangers, straps, bolts and the like. 4 Floor surface where construction does not provided a platform (e.g. floor boarding to joisted floors). 5 Thermal insulation. 6 Sundry items. 7 Where works are to be carried out by a *subcontractor, subcontractor's preliminaries*, design fees, risk allowance, overheads and profit.	1 Suspended timber floors used in lowest floor construction (included in *sub-element* 1.4.1: Ground floor slab/bed and suspended floor construction). 2 Joists and other structural members forming an integral part of a timber frame structure (included in *sub-element* 2.1.5: Timber frames). 3 Surface treatments to floor boarding (included in *sub-element* 3.2.1: Finishes to floors). 4 Applied floor finishes (included in *sub-element* 3.2.1: Finishes to floors). 5 Balustrades and handrails to internal balconies, walkways, atriums, and the like (included in *element* 2.7: Internal walls and partitions). 6 Applied ceiling finishes and linings (included in *sub-element* 3.3.1: Finishes to ceilings). 7 False ceilings and demountable suspended ceilings (included in *sub-element* 3.3.2: False ceilings or 3.3.3: Demountable suspended ceilings, as appropriate). 8 Roofs to internal buildings which are not an integral part of the upper floor construction, (included in *sub-element* 3.3.2: False ceilings). 9 Balconies which are not an integral part of the upper floor construction (included in *sub-element* 2.2.5: Balconies). 10 Drainage to balconies which are an integral part of the upper floor construction (included in *sub-element* 2.2.6: Drainage to balconies).

Sub-element	Component	Unit	Measurement rules for components	Included	Excluded
4 Structural screeds **Definition:** Structural screeds.	1 Structural screed: details, including thickness (mm), reinforcement rate (kg/m³) and surface treatments, to be stated.	m²	C1 The area measured is the area to which screed is applied. The area is measured using the rules of measurement for ascertaining the gross internal floor area (GIFA). C2 Where more than one thickness of screed is employed, the area for each screed is measured. C3 Where more than one screed is employed, the combined area of each screed type shall equal the total area of the upper floors. C4 Areas of balconies, galleries, tiered terraces, walkways, internal bridges, external links, and roofs to internal buildings shall be shown separately. C5 Sloping surfaces to be measured flat on plan. **Note:** Where balconies are included, the area of the upper ground floor and lowest ground floor will exceed the GIFA. C6 Work to existing buildings is to be described and identified separately.	1 Screed. 2 Reinforcement. 3 Worked finishes. 4 Surface treatments (e.g. surface hardeners and non-slip inserts). 5 Sundry items. 6 Where works are to be carried out by a *subcontractor, subcontractor's preliminaries,* design fees, risk allowance, overheads and profit.	1 Non-structural screeds (included in *sub-element* 3.2.1: Finishes to floors).
5 Balconies **Definition:** Internal and external balconies which are not an integral part of the upper floor construction.	1 Balconies: details, including floor area (m²) of balcony, to be stated.	nr	C1 Where components are to be enumerated, the number of components is to be stated. C2 Work to existing buildings is to be described and identified separately.	1 Purpose made balconies, which are not an integral part of the upper floor construction. Comprising bolt-on frame, decking, soffit panels, integral drainage/drainage trays and balustrades/handrails. 2 Protective coatings and paint systems. 3 Surface treatments (e.g. surface hardeners and non-slip inserts). 4 Fittings and fixings. 5 Sundry items. 6 Where works are to be carried out by a *subcontractor, subcontractor's preliminaries,* design fees, risk allowance, overheads and profit.	1 Proprietary bolt-on balconies (e.g. 'Juliet' balconies – included in *sub-element* 2.5.4: Subsidiary walls, balustrades, handrails, railings and proprietary balconies). 2 Low level and dwarf walls, balustrades, handrails and railings to external walkways which form an integral part of the building envelope and the like (included in *sub-element* 2.5.4: Subsidiary walls, balustrades, handrails, railings and proprietary balconies). 3 Drainage to balconies which is not an integral part of the balcony unit (included in *sub-element* 2.2.6: Drainage to balconies).

Sub-element	Component	Unit	Measurement rules for components	Included	Excluded
6 Drainage to balconies **Definition:** Piped internal or external disposal systems for taking rainwater from balconies to the first underground drain connection or gully.	1 Rainwater pipes: details to be stated. 2 Floor outlets: details to be stated.	m nr	C1 Where components are to be enumerated, the number of components is to be stated. C2 The length of linear components measured is their extreme length, over all fittings, branches and the like. C3 Work to existing buildings is to be described and identified separately.	1 Rainwater downpipes, including bends, swan necks and rainwater shoes and the like. 2 Floor outlets. 3 Testing and commissioning of above ground surface water drainage systems. 4 Sundry items. 5 Where works are to be carried out by a *subcontractor, subcontractor's preliminaries*, design fees, risk allowance, overheads and profit.	1 Drainage to external walkways and the like (included in *sub-element* 2.5.4: Subsidiary walls, balustrades, handrails, railings and proprietary balconies). 2 Surface water drainage beyond the first underground drain connection or gully (included in *element* 8.6: External drainage).

Element 2.3: Roof

Sub-element	Component	Unit	Measurement rules for components	Included	Excluded
1 Roof structure **Definition:** All components of the roof structure.	1 Roof structure – pitched roofs: details, including design loads (kN/m²), spans (m) and angle of pitch (°), to be stated. 2 Extra over roof structure – pitched roofs for forming dormer. 3 Roof structure – flat roofs: details, including design loads (kN/m²) and spans (m), to be stated.	m² m² m²	C1 The area measured for pitched roofs is the area of the roof on plan, to the extremities of the eaves. C2 The area measured for dormers is the area of the dormer on plan, to the extremities of the eaves and valleys. C3 Flat roofs (without parapet walls): The area measured is the area of the roof on plan, to the extremities of the eaves. C4 Flat roofs (with parapet walls): The area measured is the area within the parapet walls measured to the internal face of the parapet walls to the roof. **Note:** Roof housings (e.g. lift and motor and plant rooms). These shall be broken down into the appropriate constituent *components* and measured in accordance with the measurement rules for the applicable *components*.	1 Roof decks and slabs. 2 Trusses, purlins, rafters, binders, hangers, hip and valley rafters, ridge boards, wall plates, firrings, ceiling joists and the like. 3 Dormer trusses. 4 Specialist *subcontractor/supplier* design of roof trusses. 5 Roof boarding. 6 Beams which form an integral part of the roof in a framed building. 7 Carpenter's metalwork, including connectors, bracings, straps, hangers, strutting, joist hangers, bolts and the like. 8 Eaves and verge structure. 9 Gable ends and internal walls above wall plate level forming part of the roof construction.	1 Dormer coverings and windows to dormers (included in *sub-elements* 2.3.2: Roof coverings and 2.6.1: External windows, as appropriate). 2 Basement roofs acting as a podium slab or transfer slab (included in *element* 2.2: Upper floors, as appropriate). 3 Parapet wall, including copings and cappings (included in *element* 2.5: External walls). 4 Roof platforms integral to framing system such as off-site manufactured timber frames or panel systems (included in *element* 2.1.5: Timber frames). 5 Gable ends formed as part of the external wall construction (included in *element* 2.5: External walls). 6 Internal walls in roof formed as part of the internal walls construction (included in *element* 2.7: Internal walls and partitions).

Sub-element	Component	Unit	Measurement rules for components	Included	Excluded
			C5 Work to existing buildings is to be described and identified separately.	10 Concrete, reinforcement, formwork (temporary and permanent) and worked finishes. 11 Precast/composite decking systems, including concrete components, in-situ concrete, site fixed formwork and reinforcement, filler units, fixing slips, metal clips and other fixings, joints (including grouting joints), worked finishes and performance tests. 12 Basement roofs (i.e. where not acting as a podium slab or transfer slab). 13 Roofs to internal buildings. 14 Beams in unframed buildings. 15 Structural screeds to roofs, including reinforcement and worked finishes. 16 Permanent formwork. 17 Thermal insulation laid in roof space (e.g. laid between or over ceiling joists). 18 Sundry items. 19 Where works are to be carried out by a subcontractor, subcontractor's preliminaries, design fees, risk allowance, overheads and profit.	7 Chimneys (included in element 2.5: External walls or element 2.7: Internal walls and partitions, as appropriate). 8 Roofs to internal buildings (included in element 2.2: Upper floors or element 2.3: Roof, as appropriate). 9 Canopies to external areas (included in sub-element 8.8.3: Ancillary buildings and structures). 10 Canopies to external doors (included in sub-element 2.6.2: External doors). 11 Horizontal solar/rainscreen systems providing protection to external walls (included in sub-element 2.5.3: Solar/rainscreen cladding).
2 Roof coverings **Definition:** Protective cladding, coverings and coatings to roofs.	1 Roof coverings, non-structural screeds, thermal insulation, and surface treatments: details to be stated. 2 Extra over roof coverings for coverings to dormers, including cladding to dormer cheeks.	m² m²	C1 The area to be measured for roof coverings and the like is the surface area of the roof covering to the extremities of the eaves or to the internal face of the parapet wall, whichever is applicable, excluding the area of rooflights, skylights and openings. No deduction is made for voids less than 1.00m². C2 The area to be measured for dormer coverings is the surface area of the dormer roof coverings to the extremities of the eaves. No deduction is made for voids less than 1.00m².	1 Roof cladding/coverings (e.g. tiling, slating, sheet coverings and thatching), including battening, underlay, vapour control layers, hip, valley, eaves and verge treatment, flashings, edge trims and other components required for the applicable cladding/covering system. 2 Mastic asphalt roofing, liquid applied roof coatings and built up felt roof coverings, including underlay, vapour control layers, flashings, edge trims, skirtings, upstands and other boundary work, and other components required for the applicable roof covering system.	1 Dormer construction and windows to dormers (included in sub-elements 2.3.1: Roof structure and 2.6.1: External windows, as appropriate). 2 Vertical cladding to walls where of the same construction as the roof (included in element 2.5: External walls). 3 Structural screeds to roofs (included in sub-element 2.3.1: Roof structure). 4 Finishes to ceilings under roof structure (included in sub-element 3.3.1: Finishes to ceilings).

Sub-element	Component	Unit	Measurement rules for components	Included	Excluded
	3 Eaves, verge treatment to pitched roofs: details to be stated.	m	C3 Where more than one type of roof covering system is employed, the area measured for each system is the area covered by the system. C4 The length of linear components measured is their extreme length.	3 Photovoltaic devices (e.g. tiles, slates, profiled sheets) where an integral part of a roof covering system. 4 Roof ventilation tiles. 5 Non-structural screeds to roofs, including reinforcement and worked finishes. 6 Thermal insulation to roofs, including insulation overlays for inverted roofs. 7 Surface treatments to roof coverings (e.g. solar reflective painting, chippings and the like). 8 Paving tiles, paving slabs and the like, to form service walkways, roof terraces and the like on roof surfaces. 9 Green roofs and roof gardens, including protection layer; drainage layer; filter membranes and growing medium. 10 Planting to green roofs/roof gardens. 11 Sundry items. 12 Where works are to be carried out by a subcontractor, subcontractor's preliminaries, design fees, risk allowance, overheads and profit.	5 False ceilings and suspended ceilings under roof structure (included in sub-element 3.3.2: False ceilings or 3.3.3 Demountable suspended ceilings, as appropriate). 6 Solar water collectors, heating panels and the like (included in sub-element 5.8.6: Transformation devices). 7 Photovoltaic tiles, panels and the like where not an integral part of the roof covering system (included in sub-element 5.8.6: Transformation devices). 8 Roof and smoke vents (included in sub-element 2.3.5: Rooflights, skylights and openings).
	4 Edge treatment to flat roofs: details stated.	m	C5 Curved work is to be described and identified separately. C6 Work to existing buildings is to be described and identified separately.		
	5 Flashings: details to be stated.	m			
3 Glazed roofs **Definition:** Glazed roofing systems.	1 Glazed roof: details to be stated.	m²	C1 The area measured is the area of the glazed roof on plan. C2 Curved work is to be described and identified separately. C3 Work to existing buildings is to be described and identified separately.	1 Patent glazing. 2 Glazed roofing systems. 3 Perspex roofing systems. 4 Roof components, including flashings, cover strips, integral drainage channels, perimeter treatments and the like. 5 Sundry items. 6 Where works are to be carried out by a subcontractor, subcontractor's preliminaries, design fees, risk allowance, overheads and profit.	1 Rooflights and other glazed openings (included in sub-element 2.3.5: Rooflights, skylights and openings).

Sub-element	Component	Unit	Measurement rules for components	Included	Excluded
4 Roof drainage **Definition:** Piped internal or external disposal systems for taking rainwater from roofs and the like to the first underground drain connection or gully.	1 Gutters: details to be stated.	m	C1 The length of linear components measured is their extreme length, over all fittings, branches and the like. C2 Other cost significant components are to be described and identified separately. Such components are to be measured by area (m²), linear measurement (m) or enumerated (nr) separately. C3 Curved work is to be described and identified separately. C4 Work to existing buildings is to be described and identified separately.	1 Gutters (other than those forming an integral part of a cladding or curtain walling system), including fittings, gutter outlets, balloons and gratings to outlets, and the like. 2 Rainwater downpipes, including bends, swan necks and rainwater shoes. 3 Syphonic roof drainage pipework systems. 4 Rainwater heads, including gratings. 5 Painting and anti-corrosion treatments to gutters and rainwater downpipes. 6 Testing and commissioning of above ground surface water drainage systems. 7 Sundry items. 8 Where works are to be carried out by a subcontractor, subcontractor's preliminaries, design fees, risk allowance, overheads and profit.	1 Gutters forming an integral part of a roof structure (included in sub-element 2.3.1: Roof structure). 2 Gutters forming an integral part of a cladding or curtain walling system (included in element 2.5: External walls, as appropriate). 3 Gutters and rainwater pipes to balconies and canopies (included in sub-element 2.2.6: Drainage to balconies, sub-element 2.6.1: External windows or sub-element 2.6.2: External doors, as appropriate). 4 Rainwater harvesting systems (included in sub-element 5.4.2: Cold water distribution). 5 Surface water drainage beyond the first underground drainage connection or gully (included in sub-element 8.6.1: Surface water and foul water drainage).
	2 Rainwater pipes: details to be stated.	m			
5 Rooflights, skylights and openings **Definition:** Rooflights, skylights and openings to roof.	1 Rooflights, skylights and openings: type and size to be stated.	nr/m²	C1 Where components are to be enumerated, the number of components is to be stated. C2 The area measured is the area of rooflights, skylights and openings. C3 Curved work is to be described and identified separately. C4 Work to existing buildings is to be described and identified separately.	1 Rooflights, skylights and the like. 2 Opening gear, frames, kerbs and glazing. 3 Sun pipes/tubes. 4 Pavement lights. 5 Roof hatches. 6 Access hatches to roof spaces. 7 Smoke vents. 8 Roof vents and roof cowls. 9 Sundry items. 10 Where works are to be carried out by a subcontractor, subcontractor's preliminaries, design fees, risk allowance, overheads and profit.	1 Dormer roofs and windows (included in sub-elements 2.3.1: Roof structure, 2.3.2: Roof coverings and 2.6.1: External windows, as appropriate). 2 Access hatches to false ceilings or demountable suspended ceilings (included in sub-element 3.3.2: False ceilings or 3.3.3: Demountable suspended ceilings, as appropriate). 3 Flashings to rooflights, skylights and openings (included in sub-element 2.3.2: Roof coverings).

Sub-element	Component	Unit	Measurement rules for components	Included	Excluded
6 Roof features **Definition:** Roof features not forming part of the main roof structure.	1 Roof features: details to be stated.	nr	C1 Where components are to be enumerated, the number of components is to be stated. C2 Work to existing buildings is to be described and identified separately.	1 Turrets. 2 Wind vanes. 3 Spires. 4 False chimneys. 5 Enclosures designed solely to conceal plant, rooflines, and the like (complete structure including wall louvers). 6 Fall arrest systems. 7 Access systems for cleaning roof. 8 Roof edge protection (permanent). 9 Balustrades, handrails and the like to roof edges and walkways. 10 Service walkways within roof voids. 11 Sundry items. 12 Where works are to be carried out by a subcontractor, *subcontractor's preliminaries*, design fees, risk allowance, overheads and profit.	1 Finials (included in *sub-element* 5.11.2: Lightning protection). 2 Building Maintenance Units (BMUs – included in *sub-element* 2.5.5: Facade access/cleaning systems). 3 Facade access systems (included in *sub-element* 2.5.5: Facade access/cleaning systems). 4 Roof top wind turbines and wind energy systems (included in *sub-element* 5.8.6: Transformation devices). 5 Photovoltaic tiles, panels and the like (included in *sub-element* 5.8.6: Transformation devices). 6 Solar water collectors, heating panels and the like (included in *sub-element* 5.8.6: Transformation devices).

Element 2.4: Stairs and ramps

Sub-element	Component	Unit	Measurement rules for components	Included	Excluded
1 Stair/ramp structures **Definition:** Construction of staircases, ramps and landings.	1 Stair structures: details, including vertical rise of staircase, to be stated. 2 Ramp structures: details, including vertical rise of ramp, to be stated.	nr nr	C1 Number of storey flights (i.e. the number of staircases or ramps multiplied by the number of floors served (excluding the lowest floor served in each case). C2 The vertical rise of stairs or ramps is the distance measured from top of structural floor level to top of structural floor level. C3 Curved work is to be described and identified separately. C4 Work to existing buildings is to be described and identified separately.	1 Staircases, including spiral staircases and the like. 2 Access ramps. 3 Landings between floor levels. 4 Fire escape staircases. 5 In-situ and precast concrete, including concrete, reinforcement, formwork, worked finishes and grouting (of precast units). 6 Staircases fabricated from steel, timber or other material, including off-site applied coatings and paint systems. 7 Sundry items. 8 Where works are to be carried out by a *subcontractor, subcontractor's preliminaries, design fees, risk allowance, overheads and profit.*	1 Landings at floor levels (included in *element* 2.2: Upper floors, as appropriate). 2 Ramps which are an integral part of the floor construction levels (included in *sub-element* 2.4: Ground slab/bed and suspended floor construction or *element* 2.2: Upper floors, as appropriate). 3 Walls forming stairwells (included in *element* 1.3: Basement retaining walls; *element* 2.5: External walls or *element* 2.7: Internal walls and partitions, as appropriate). 4 Access and escape ladders, chutes, slides and the like (included in *sub-element* 2.4.4: Ladders/chutes/slides).
2 Stair/ramp finishes **Definition:** Finishes to stairs, ramps and landings.	1 Stair finishes: details, including vertical rise of staircase, to be stated. 2 Ramp finishes: details, including vertical rise of ramp, to be stated.	nr nr	C1 Number of storey flights (i.e. the number of staircases or ramps multiplied by the number of floors served, excluding the lowest floor served in each case). C2 The vertical rise of stairs or ramps is the distance measured from top of structural floor level to top of structural floor level. C3 Curved work is to be described and identified separately. C4 Work to existing buildings is to be described and identified separately.	1 Finishes to treads and risers. 2 Finishes to landings between floor levels. 3 Finishes to ramp surfaces. 4 Finishes to strings. 5 Finishes to the soffits of staircases. 6 Sundry items. 7 Where works are to be carried out by a *subcontractor, subcontractor's preliminaries, design fees, risk allowance, overheads and profit.*	1 Finishes to landings at floor levels (included in *element*: 3.2: Floor finishes). 2 Finishes to stairwells (included in *group element* 3: Internal finishes, as appropriate).

Sub-element	Component	Unit	Measurement rules for components	Included	Excluded
3 Stair/ramp balustrades and handrails **Definition:** Balustrades and handrails to stairs, ramps and landings.	1 Wall handrails: details, including vertical rise of staircase or ramp, to be stated.	nr	C1 Number of storey flights (i.e. the number of staircases or ramps multiplied by the number of floors served (excluding the lowest floor served in each case). C2 The vertical rise of stairs or ramps is the distance measured from top of structural floor level to top of structural floor level. C3 Curved work is to be described and identified separately. C4 Work to existing buildings is to be described and identified separately.	1 Balustrades and handrails to stairs. 2 Balustrades and handrails to landings between floor levels. 3 Balustrades and handrails to landings. 4 Applied coatings and paint systems. 5 Sundry items. 6 Where works are to be carried out by a subcontractor, subcontractor's preliminaries, design fees, risk allowance, overheads and profit.	1 Balustrades and handrails to internal platforms, walkways and the like (included in sub-element 2.7.2: Balustrades and handrails).
	2 Combined balustrades and handrails: details, including vertical rise of staircase or ramp, to be stated.	nr			
4 Ladders/chutes/slides **Definition:** Access and escape ladders and the like.	1 Ladders: details to be stated.	nr	C1 Where components are to be enumerated, the number of components is to be stated. C2 Work to existing buildings is to be described and identified separately.	1 Fire escape ladders. 2 Fire escape chutes/slides. 3 Access ladders. 4 Loft ladders, including hatch doors where an integral part of the loft ladder. 5 Applied coatings and paint systems. 6 Sundry items. 7 Where works are to be carried out by a subcontractor, subcontractor's preliminaries, design fees, risk allowance, overheads and profit.	
	2 Chutes: details to be stated.	nr			
	3 Slides: details to be stated.	nr			

Element 2.5: External walls

Sub-element	Component	Unit	Measurement rules for components	Included	Excluded
1 External walls above ground floor level **Definition:** External enclosing walls above ground floor level.	1 External walls: details to be stated. **Note:** Reinforcement rate (kg/m³) and formwork finish for in-situ concrete walls to be stated.	m²	C1 The area measured is the area of the external wall, measured on the centre line of the external wall. No deductions for windows or external doors. C2 Where more than one type of external wall system is employed, the area measured for each external wall system is measured separately.	1 External enclosing walls (i.e. both internal and external skins). 2 Underside of returns in external walls. 3 Parapet walls, including copings and cappings, to roofs formed as part of the external walls. 4 Gable walls formed as part of the wall construction.	1 Columns and beams, which form an integral part of the structural frame (included in element 2.1: Frame, as appropriate). 2 Concrete walls, core walls and the like where an integral part of the structural frame (included in sub-element 2.1.4: Concrete frames).

Sub-element	Component	Unit	Measurement rules for components	Included	Excluded
	2 Extra over external walls for plinths, cornices, ornamental bands and the like: details to be stated.	m	C3 Where more than one external wall system is employed, the combined area of each external wall system shall equal the total area of all external wall systems. C4 The area measured for external wall finishes is the surface area of the external wall component to which the finish is to be applied.	5 Chimneys forming part of external walls. 6 Columns and beams in unframed structures. 7 Curtain walling (designed and fixed as an integrated assembly – complete with opening lights, doors, ventilators, and the like). 8 Structural glazing assemblies and the like (i.e. glazing that forms an integral part of a cladding system).	3 Walls provided by framing system such as off-site manufactured timber frames or tunnel form (included in element 2.1: Frame). 4 Roof structures and cladding (included in element 2.3: Roof). 5 Gable ends, internal walls and chimneys above plate level formed as part of the roof construction (included in element 2.3: Roof).
	3 Extra over external walls for quoins: details to bed stated.	m	C5 Other cost significant sub-components, such as decorative masonry or brickwork bands/panels; or cover strips and window boards which form an integral part of internal skins/backing walls to curtain walling systems, cladding systems and the like, are to be measured by area (m²), linear measurement (m) or enumerated (nr) and identified separately.	9 Profiled sheet cladding systems, including cladding rails and the like. 10 Photovoltaic glazing or cladding panels where an integral part of a curtain walling system, or structural glazing assemblies or profiled sheet cladding systems. 10 Rigid sheet cladding systems, including support framework.	6 Windows and doors (included in element 2.6: Windows and external doors). 7 Applied finishes to inner faces of external walls, including dry lining systems (included in sub-element 3.1.1: Finishes to walls). 8 False ceilings and demountable suspended ceilings forming external soffits (included in sub-element 2.5.4: External soffits).
	4 Extra over external walls for forming openings for windows: details, including overall size of opening (mm), to be stated.	nr	C6 The length of linear components measured is their extreme length, over all obstructions. C7 Descriptions shall include the amount of any PC Sum included in the unit rates applied to the item.	11 Panelled walling systems, including panels to a frame structure. 12 Internal skins/backing walls to curtain walling systems, cladding systems, walling systems and the like, including window boards, cover strips and the like. 13 Concrete walls, including reinforcement and formwork.	9 Applied finishes to external soffits (included in sub-element 2.5.4: External soffits). 10 Retaining walls to basements (included in element 1.3: Basement retaining walls, as appropriate).
	5 Extra over external walls for forming openings for external doors: details, including overall size of opening (mm), to be stated.	nr	C8 Curved work is to be described and identified separately. C9 Work to existing buildings is to be described and identified separately.	14 Masonry walls (i.e. brickwork, blockwork and stonework), including forming cavities, wall ties, thermal insulation and the like. 15 Plinths, cornices, ornamental bands and quoins which are formed with a different material from general wall. 16 Lightweight steel frame systems, including cladding and insulation.	11 Walls to roof enclosures designed solely to conceal plant, tank rooms, and the like (included in sub-element 2.3.5: Roof features). 12 Walls and railings to external walkways and balconies built of the upper floor construction (included in sub-element 2.5.5: Subsidiary walls, balustrades, handrails, railings and proprietary balconies).
	6 Finishes applied to external walls: details to be stated.	m²		17 Thermal insulation, membranes, and the like. 18 Timber and plastic cladding systems (e.g. weatherboarding). 19 Insulating render systems.	13 Railings to parapet walls (included in sub-element 2.5.5: Subsidiary walls, balustrades, handrails, railings and proprietary balconies). 14 Work in retaining facades to existing buildings (included in sub-element 7.4.1: Facade retention works).

Sub-element	Component	Unit	Measurement rules for components	Included	Excluded
				20 Finishes applied to external wall (e.g. paint systems, coating systems, ceramic/stone cladding, tiling and other materials). 21 Finishes to underside of returns in external walls. 22 Planted 'green' walls, including protection layer, drainage layer, filter membranes and growing medium. 23 Forming openings in external walls for external windows and external doors, including lintels/beams, head courses, damp-proof courses, cavity trays, closing cavities and all other work to soffits, sills and reveals of openings. 24 Sundry items. 25 Where works are to be carried out by a subcontractor, subcontractor's preliminaries, design fees, risk allowance, overheads and profit.	15 Common user access scaffolding (included in group element 10: Main contractor's preliminaries).
2 External walls below ground level **Definition:** External enclosing walls below ground floor level that are not formed by retaining walls.	1 External walls: details to be stated. **Note:** Reinforcement rate (kg/m³) and formwork finish for in-situ concrete walls to be stated. 2 Extra over external walls for plinths, cornices, ornamental bands and the like: details to be stated. 3 Extra over external walls for quoins: details to be stated.	m² m m	C1 The area measured is the area of the external wall, measured on the centre line of the external wall. No deductions for windows or external doors. C2 Where more than one type of external wall system is employed, the area measured for each external wall system is measured separately. C3 Where more than one external wall system is employed, the combined area of each external wall system shall equal the total area of all external wall systems. C4 The area measured for external wall finishes is the surface area of the external wall component to which the finish is to be applied.	1 External basement walls below ground floor level not in contact with earthwork or part of an embedded retaining wall construction (i.e. not retaining walls). 2 External enclosing walls (i.e. both internal and external skins). 3 Underside of returns in external walls. 4 Parapet walls, including copings and cappings, to roofs formed as part of the external walls. 5 Gable walls formed as part of the wall construction. 6 Chimneys forming part of external walls. 7 Columns and beams in unframed structures. 8 Curtain walling (designed and fixed as an integrated assembly – complete with opening lights, doors, ventilators, and the like).	1 Basement excavation (included in element 1.2: Basement excavation). 2 Temporary or permanent support to the excavation, e.g. caissons, sheet piling, continuous piling, and the like (included in element 1.2: Basement excavation). 3 Basement wall construction, where wall in contact with earthwork (included in element 1.2: Basement excavation). 4 Embedded basement retaining wall construction (included in sub-element 1.3.2: Embedded basement retaining walls). 5 Columns and beams, which form an integral part of the structural frame (included in element 2.1: Frame, as appropriate).

Sub-element	Component	Unit	Measurement rules for components	Included	Excluded
	4 Extra over external walls for forming openings for windows: details, including overall size of opening (mm), to be stated.	nr	C5 Other cost significant sub-components, such as cover strips and window boards which form an integral part of internal skins/backing walls to curtain walling systems, cladding systems and the like, are to be measured by area (m²), linear measurement (m) or enumerated (nr) and identified separately.	9 Structural glazing assemblies and the like (i.e. glazing that forms an integral part of a cladding system).	6 Concrete walls, core walls and the like where an integral part of the structural frame (included in sub-element 2.1.4: Concrete frames).
				10 Profiled sheet cladding systems, including cladding rails and the like.	7 Walls provided by framing system such as off-site manufactured timber frames or tunnel form (included in element 2.1: Frame).
	5 Extra over external walls for forming openings for external doors: details, including overall size of opening (mm), to be stated.	nr	C6 The length of linear components measured is their extreme length, over all obstructions. C7 Descriptions shall include the amount of any PC Sum included in the unit rates applied to the item.	11 Photovoltaic glazing or cladding panels where an integral part of a curtain walling system, or structural glazing assemblies or profiled sheet cladding systems.	8 Applied finishes to inner faces of external walls including dry lining systems (included in sub-element 3.1.1: Finishes to walls).
			C8 Curved work is to be described and identified separately.	12 Rigid sheet cladding systems, including support framework.	
			C9 Work to existing buildings is to be described and identified separately.	13 Panelled walling systems, including panels to a frame structure.	
	6 Finishes to external walls: details to be stated.	m²		14 Internal skins/backing walls to curtain walling systems, cladding systems, walling systems and the like, including window boards, cover strips and the like.	
				15 Concrete walls, including reinforcement and formwork.	
				16 Masonry walls (i.e. brickwork, blockwork and stonework), including forming cavities, wall ties, thermal insulation and the like.	
				17 Plinths, cornices, ornamental bands and quoins which are formed with a different material from general wall.	
				18 Lightweight steel frame systems, including cladding and insulation.	
				19 Thermal insulation, membranes, and the like.	
				20 Timber and plastic cladding systems (e.g. weatherboarding).	
				21 Insulating render systems.	
				22 Finishes applied to external wall (e.g. paint systems, coating systems, ceramic/stone cladding, tiling and other materials.	
				23 Finishes to underside of returns in external walls.	

Sub-element	Component	Unit	Measurement rules for components	Included	Excluded
				24 Planted 'green' walls, including protection layer, drainage layer, filter membranes and growing medium. 25 Forming openings in external walls for external windows and external doors, including lintels/beams, head courses, damp-proof courses, cavity trays, closing cavities and all other work to soffits, sills and reveals of openings. 26 Sundry items. 27 Where works are to be carried out by a *subcontractor, subcontractor's preliminaries,* design fees, risk allowance, overheads and profit.	
3 Solar/rainscreen cladding **Definition:** Cladding systems and the like attached to the exterior of the building to protect the external walls.	1 Vertical solar/rainscreen cladding: details to be stated.	m²	C1 The area measured is the area of the overcladding system. C2 Where more than one type of overcladding system is employed, the area for each overcladding system is measured.	1 Vertical and horizontal exterior overcladding systems, including support system. 2 'Brise Soleil' and the like, including support systems. 3 Sundry items.	1 External shutters, integral to blinds to windows, canopies and the like, providing protection to windows and doors (included in *element 2.6:* Windows and external doors).
	2 Horizontal solar/rainscreen cladding: details to be stated.	m	C3 The length of linear components measured is their extreme length, over all obstructions. C4 Curved work is to be described and identified separately. C5 Work to existing buildings is to be described and identified separately.	4 Where works are to be carried out by a *subcontractor, subcontractor's preliminaries,* design fees, risk allowance, overheads and profit.	
4 External soffits **Definition:** External false ceilings and demountable suspended ceilings which form an integral part of the building envelope.	1 External soffit: details to be stated.	m²	C1 The area measured for each type of external soffit is the surface area of the soffit to which the finish is to be applied. C2 The area measured for each type of finish applied to external soffits is the surface area of the soffit to which the finish is to be applied.	1 In-situ/board ceilings, including soffit linings and battens, fixed direct to underside of upper floor construction. 2 Demountable suspended ceiling systems, including suspension system. 3 Insulation; fixed direct to underside of upper floor construction or laid on soffit construction.	1 False ceilings to internal ceilings (included in *sub-element 3.3.2:* False ceilings). 2 Applied finishes to internal false ceilings (included in *sub-element 3.3.1:* Finishes to ceilings). 3 Demountable suspending ceilings to internal ceilings (included in *sub-element 3.3.3:* Demountable suspended ceilings).
	2 Cornices, covings and the like: details to be stated.	m	C3 The length of linear components measured is their extreme length, over all obstructions.		
	3 Shadow gaps and the like: details to be stated.	m	C4 Other cost significant components to be described and measured by area (m²), linear measurement (m) or enumerated (nr) separately, as appropriate.	4 In-situ coatings applied to false ceilings (e.g. plaster skim coats, render, roughcast, and specialist coatings).	

Sub-element	Component	Unit	Measurement rules for components	Included	Excluded
	4 Access hatches and the like: details to be stated.	nr	C5 Descriptions shall include the amount of any PC Sum included in the unit rates applied to the item. C6 Curved work is to be described and identified separately. C7 Work to existing buildings is to be described and identified separately.	5 Painting and decorating to false ceilings. 6 Cornices, covings and the like. 7 Shadow gaps and the like, including painting. 8 Access hatches and the like in external soffit construction. 9 Sundry items. 10 Where works are to be carried out by a *subcontractor, subcontractor's preliminaries,* design fees, risk allowance, overheads and profit.	
	5 Finishes applied to external soffits: details to be stated.	m²			
5 Subsidiary walls, balustrades, handrails, railings and proprietary balconies **Definition:** Subsidiary components which form an integral part of the building envelope.	1 Walls: details to be stated.	m	C1 Where components are to be enumerated, the number of components is to be stated. C2 The length of linear components measured is their extreme length, over all obstructions. C3 Where more than one type of component is employed, each component is measured. C4 Other cost significant components to be described and identified separately. Such components are to be measured by area (m²), linear measurement (m) or enumerated (nr) separately. C5 Curved work is to be described and identified separately. C6 Work to existing buildings is to be described and identified separately.	1 Low level or dwarf walls, balustrades, handrails and railings to external walkways and balconies built off the upper floor construction, which form an integral part of the building envelope (e.g. to provide walkway between external enclosing wall and edge of upper floor construction), including walls forming planters. 2 Walls forming planters, including protection layer, drainage layer, filter membranes and growing medium. 3 Wall handrails. 4 Combined balustrades and handrails. 5 Railings and barriers to tops of parapet walls. 6 Proprietary bolt-on balconies (e.g. 'Juliet' balconies). 7 Surface water drainage from external walkways and the like attached to building to first underground drain connection or gully, including floor outlets. 8 All work, materials, components and the like required to construct subsidiary components.	1 Surface water drainage beyond the first underground drain connection or gully (included in *sub-element* 8.6.1: Surface water and foul water drainage). 2 Internal and external balconies which are an integral part of the upper floor construction (included in *element* 2.2: Upper floors, as appropriate).
	2 Walls forming planters: details to be stated.	m			
	3 Combined balustrades and handrails: details to be stated.	m			
	4 Wall mounted handrails: details to be stated.	m			
	5 Parapet railings: details to be stated.	m			
	6 Proprietary bolt-on balconies: details to be stated.	nr			

Sub-element	Component	Unit	Measurement rules for components	Included	Excluded
	7 Rainwater pipes: details to be stated.	nr/m		9 Testing and commissioning of above ground surface water drainage systems.	
	8 Floor outlets: details to be stated.	nr		10 Sundry items. 11 Where works are to be carried out by a subcontractor, subcontractor's preliminaries, design fees, risk allowance, overheads and profit.	
6 Facade access/cleaning systems **Definition:** Systems for accessing and cleaning facades.	1 Facade cleaning systems: details to be stated.	nr	C1 Where components are to be enumerated, the number of components is to be stated. C2 Work to existing buildings is to be described and identified separately.	1 Window and facade cleaning trolley/cradles (including twin track, manual and automatic systems). 2 Combined facade and roof cleaning systems. 3 Building maintenance units (BMU). 4 Other facade access systems. 5 Builder's work in connection with facade access/cleaning systems. 6 Testing and commissioning of facade access/cleaning systems. 7 Sundry items. 8 Where works are to be carried out by a subcontractor, subcontractor's preliminaries, design fees, risk allowance, overheads and profit.	1 Separate access systems for cleaning roof (included in *sub-element* 2.3.6: Roof features). 2 General purpose low voltage (LV) power supplies (included in *sub-element* 5.8.2: Power installations). 3 Building management systems and other control systems (included in *sub-element* 5.12.3: Central control/building management systems (BMS)).

Element 2.6: Windows and external doors

Sub-element	Component	Unit	Measurement rules for components	Included	Excluded
1 External windows **Definition:** Windows and openings in external walls for ventilation and light.	1 Windows: details, including overall size of opening (mm), to be stated.	m²	C1 Where the area of the component is to be measured, the area measured is the area of the component measured over frames. C2 Where more than one type of component is employed, each component is measured. C3 Other cost significant components are to be described and identified separately. Such components are to be measured by area (m²), linear measurement (m) or enumerated (nr) separately. C4 Curved work is to be described and identified separately. C5 Work to existing buildings is to be described and identified separately.	1 Windows, including opening lights, fixed lights, frames, linings, window boards, cover trims. Ironmongery and glazing. 2 Windows to dormers. 3 External shop fronts, including temporary shop fronts. 4 Roller shutters, sliding shutters, grilles and the like providing security or protection to windows and shop fronts. 5 Fly screens and storm windows. 6 Integral blinds to windows. 7 Solar/rainscreen overcladding systems to windows. 8 Photovoltaic glazing where an integral part of window system. 9 Canopies and the like providing protection to windows and shop fronts, including any associated surface water drainage. 10 Protective film applied to windows. 11 External blinds, shutters and like. 12 Window boards, trims and the like, including those which are not an integral part of the window unit. 13 Painting and decorating. 14 Sundry items. 15 Where works are to be carried out by a subcontractor, subcontractor's preliminaries, design fees, risk allowance, overheads and profit.	1 Forming openings for external windows, shop fronts, roller shutters and the like (included in sub-element 2.5.1: External walls above ground floor level or 2.5.2: External walls below ground floor level, as appropriate). 2 Construction of and coverings to dormer windows (included in sub-elements 2.3.1: Roof structure and 2.3.2: Roof coverings). 3 Glazing that forms an integral part of a cladding system, e.g. structural glazing and curtain walling (included in element 2.5: External walls, as appropriate). 4 Roller shutters, sliding shutters, grilles and the like, where performing the function of an external door (included in sub-element 2.6.2 External doors). 5 Solar/rainscreen cladding to external walls (included in sub-element 2.5.3: Solar/rainscreen cladding).
	2 Shop fronts: details, including overall size of opening (mm), to be stated.	m²			
	3 Roller shutters, sliding shutters, grilles and the like to window openings: details, including overall size of opening (mm), to be stated.	nr			

Sub-element	Component	Unit	Measurement rules for components	Included	Excluded
2 External doors **Definition:** Doors and openings in external enclosing walls.	1 External doors: details, including type, number of door leaves (nr), size of each door leaf (mm) and overall size of opening (mm), to be stated.	nr	C1 Where components are to be enumerated, the number of components is to be stated. C2 Where the area of component is to be measured, the area measured is the area of the component measured over frames. C3 The length of linear components measured is their extreme length. C4 Where more than one type of component is employed, each component is measured. C5 Other cost significant components are to be described and identified separately. Such components are to be measured by area (m²), linear measurement (m) or enumerated (nr) separately. C6 Curved work is to be described and identified separately. C7 Work to existing buildings is to be described and identified separately.	1 Entrance doors, door frames, door linings, door sets. Including solid, glazed and partially glazed doors, louver doors, and the like. Proprietary and purpose-made. 2 Entrance screens and doors, including frames. 3 Revolving doors. 4 Patio doors. 5 Garage doors. 6 Rolling and sliding shutters, including integral access doors. 7 External shop front doors. 8 Manual and automatic doors. 9 Canopies and the like, providing protection to external doors, including any associated surface water drainage. 10 Grilles (fixed and folding) and the like providing security or protection to doors. 11 Fanlights, sidelights and side panels integral to external door. 12 Architraves. 13 Ironmongery, including door closers, panic locks and the like. 14 Glazed vision panels. 15 Painting and decorating. 16 Fly screens and storm doors. 17 Integral blinds to doors. 18 Solar/rainscreen overcladding to doors. 19 Canopies and the like, providing protection to doors. 20 Sundry items. 21 Where works are to be carried out by a *subcontractor, subcontractor's preliminaries*, design fees, risk allowance, overheads and profit.	1 Forming openings for external doors, shop front doors, roller shutters and the like (included in *sub-element* 2.5.1: External walls above ground floor level or 2.5.2: External walls below ground floor level, as appropriate). 2 Enclosed porches. To be broken down into the appropriate constituent *sub-elements* and measured in accordance with the appropriate measurement rules. 3 Canopies to external areas (included in *sub-element* 8.8.3: Ancillary buildings and structures).
	2 Revolving doors: details, including overall size of opening (mm), to be stated.	nr			
	3 Shop front doors: details, including type, number of door leaves (nr), size of each door leaf (mm) and overall size of opening (mm), to be stated.	nr			
	4 Roller shutters, sliding shutters and the like to external door openings: details, including overall size of opening (mm), to be stated.	nr			
	5 Garage doors: details, including overall size of opening (mm), to be stated.	nr			
	6 Canopies: details to be stated.	nr			
	7 Grilles: details, including overall size of opening (mm), to be stated.	nr			
	8 Architraves: details to be stated.	m			

Element 2.7: Internal walls and partitions

Sub-element	Component	Unit	Measurement rules for components	Included	Excluded
1 Walls and partitions **Definition:** Internal walls and fixed partitions.	1 Internal walls: details, including thickness, to be stated.	m²	C1 The area measured is the area of internal walls and partitions, measured on the centre line of the internal wall or partition. No deduction is made for door openings, screens or the like.	1 Internal walls, including full height and low level walls.	1 Internal skin of external walls (included in *element* 2.5: External walls).
	2 Extra over internal walls for forming openings in walls for internal doors and the like: details, including overall size of opening (mm), to be stated.	nr	C2 Where more than one type of component is employed, each component is measured. C3 Other cost significant components are to be described and identified separately. Such components are to be measured by area (m²), linear measurement (m) or enumerated (nr) separately.	2 Fixed partitions, including demountable partition systems. 3 Internal shop fronts and the like, including temporary shop fronts. 4 Columns and beams which are not an integral part of a frame structure. 5 Internal walls in roof formed as part of the wall construction. 6 Walls forming chimneys, stairwells and lift shafts.	2 Columns and beams, which form an integral part of the structural frame (included in *element* 2.1: Frame, as appropriate). 3 Concrete walls, core walls and the like where an integral part of the structural frame (included in *sub-element* 2.1.4: Concrete frames). 4 Walls provided by framing system such as off-site manufactured timber frames or tunnel form (included in *element* 2.1: Frame).
	3 Fixed partitions: details, including thickness, to be stated.	m²	C4 Curved work is to be described and identified separately. C5 Work to existing buildings is to be described and identified separately.	7 Walls forming cubicles. 8 Walls forming planters, including protection layer, drainage layer, filter membranes and growing medium. 9 Borrowed lights, glazed screens and the like which are an integral part of internal walls and partitions. 10 Concrete walls, including reinforcement and formwork, which are not an integral part of the structural frame.	5 Applied wall finishes to internal walls, including dry lining systems (included in *element* 3.1.1: Finishes to walls). 6 Cubicles, i.e. proprietary pre-finished panel systems and the like (included in *sub-element* 2.7.4: Cubicles).
	4 Extra over fixed partitions for forming openings in partitions for internal doors and the like: details, including overall size of opening (mm), to be stated.	nr		11 Masonry walls (i.e. brickwork, blockwork and stonework), including floor and head support systems. 12 Timber stud partitions, including cavity insulation, board linings, filling lining joints. 13 Metal stud partitioning systems, including cavity insulation, board linings, filling lining joints. 14 Glazed partitioning. 15 Thermal insulation and membranes.	7 Special features built-in internal walls and partitions, e.g. fish tanks (included in *sub-element* 4.1.4: Works of art).

Sub-element	Component	Unit	Measurement rules for components	Included	Excluded
				16 Cappings to low level internal walls, including timber, stone, tiles and other materials. 17 Blinds, where an integral part of a proprietary partitioning system. 18 Forming openings for internal doors and the like in internal walls, including work to soffit and reveals of openings. 19 Forming openings for internal doors and the like in internal fixed partitions, including work to soffit and reveals of openings. 20 Sundry items. 21 Where works are to be carried out by a *subcontractor, subcontractor's preliminaries*, design fees, risk allowance, overheads and profit.	
2 Balustrades and handrails **Definition:** Internal balustrades, handrails and other fixed non-storey height divisions.	1 Combined balustrades and handrails: details to be stated. 2 Wall mounted handrails: details to be stated.	m m	C1 The length of linear components measured is their extreme length. C2 Where more than one type of component is employed, each component is measured. C3 Other cost significant components are to be described and identified separately. Such components are to be measured by area (m²), linear measurement (m) or enumerated (nr) separately. C4 Curved work is to be described and identified separately. C5 Work to existing buildings is to be described and identified separately.	1 Balustrades and handrails to interior atriums, access walkways, galleries and the like, including off-site and on-site applied coating and paint systems. 2 Sundry items. 3 Where works are to be carried out by a *subcontractor, subcontractor's preliminaries*, design fees, risk allowance, overheads and profit.	1 Handrails fixed to walls (included in *group element* 4: Fittings, furnishings and equipment). 2 Balustrades and handrails to stairs and staircases (included in *sub-element* 2.4.3: Stair/ramp balustrades and handrails).

Sub-element	Component	Unit	Measurement rules for components	Included	Excluded
3 Moveable room dividers **Definition:** Moveable partitions intended to divide rooms into smaller spaces.	1 Moveable room dividers and partitions: details to be stated.	m²	C1 The area measured is the area of moveable room dividers and partitions. C2 Where more than one type of component is employed, each component is measured. C3 Other cost significant components are to be described and identified separately. Such components are to be measured by area (m²), linear measurement (m) or enumerated (nr) separately. C4 Curved work is to be described and identified separately. C5 Work to existing buildings is to be described and identified separately.	1 Moveable room dividers and partitions, including frames, linings, ironmongery, architraves, cover trims and the like. Proprietary and purpose made. 2 Off-site and on-site applied coating and paint systems. 3 Sundry items. 4 Where works are to be carried out by a *subcontractor*, *subcontractor's preliminaries*, design fees, risk allowance, overheads and profit.	1 Sliding/folding doors forming an integral part of an internal wall or fixed partitions (included in *sub-element* 2.8: Internal doors).
4 Cubicles **Definition:** Proprietary pre-finished panels, assembled to form cubicles, complete with doors.	1 Cubicles: details to be stated.	nr/m²	C1 Where components are to be enumerated, the number of components is to be stated. C2 The area measured is the area of cubicles, including the area of cubicle doors. C3 Other cost significant components are to be described and identified separately. Such components are to be measured by area (m²), linear measurement (m) or enumerated (nr) separately. C4 Curved work is to be described and identified separately. C5 Work to existing buildings is to be described and identified separately.	1 Proprietary pre-finished panel cubicles (e.g. toilet and changing) and the like, including doors, trims, cover strips, ironmongery and fittings forming an integral part of the cubicle. 2 Sundry items. 3 Where works are to be carried out by a *subcontractor*, *subcontractor's preliminaries*, design fees, risk allowance, overheads and profit.	1 Internal walls and partitions performing as cubicles (included in *sub-element* 2.7.1: Walls and partitions and *element* 2.8: Internal doors, as appropriate).

Element 2.8: Internal doors

Sub-element	Component	Unit	Measurement rules for components	Included	Excluded
1 Internal doors **Definition:** Doors, hatches, shutters and grilles and other openings in internal walls and partitions.	1 Internal doors: details, including type, number of door leaves (nr), size of each door leaf (mm), and overall size of opening (mm), to be stated.	nr	C1 Where components are to be enumerated, the number of components is to be stated. C2 Where more than one type of component is employed, each component is measured. C3 Cost significant sub-components are to be described and measured linear (m) or enumerated (nr) separately, as appropriate. C4 The length of linear components measured is their extreme length. C5 Other cost significant components are to be described and identified separately. Such components are to be measured by area (m²), linear measurement (m) or enumerated (nr) separately. C6 Work to existing buildings is to be described and identified separately.	1 Doors, including standard doors, purpose made doors, full-height doors and fire resisting doors. 2 Frames, linings, architraves, stops and the like. 3 Door sets. 4 Fanlights, over-panels and sidelights and the like, integral to the door set. 5 Glazed vision panels and the like. 6 Sliding and folding doors in fixed partitions. 7 Hatches, including doors, frames, linings, architraves, stops and the like. 8 Internal roller shutters, sliding shutters, grilles and the like, including frames, linings, architraves, stops and the like. 9 Ironmongery. 10 Painting and decorating to internal doors. 11 Sundry items. 12 Where works are to be carried out by a subcontractor, subcontractor's preliminaries, design fees, risk allowance, overheads and profit.	1 Forming openings for doors in internal walls and partitions (included in sub-element 2.7.1: Walls and partitions). 2 Sliding/and folding partitions (included in sub-element 2.7.3: Moveable room dividers).
	2 Fire resisting doors: details, including type, number of door leaves (nr), fire rating (hours), size of each door leaf (mm), and overall size of opening (mm), to be stated.	nr			
	3 Door sets: details, including type, number of door leaves (nr), size of each door leaf (mm), and overall size of opening (mm), to be stated.	nr			
	4 Composite door and sidelights/over panel units: details, including type, number of door leaves (nr), size of each door leaf (mm), and overall size of opening (mm), to be stated.	nr			
	5 Roller shutters, sliding shutters, grilles and the like: details, including overall size of opening (mm), to be stated.	nr			
	6 Architraves: details to be stated.	m			

Group element 3: Internal finishes

Group element 3 comprises the following elements:

3.1 Wall finishes

3.2 Floor finishes

3.3 Ceiling finishes

Element 3.1: Wall finishes

Sub-element	Component	Unit	Measurement rules for components	Included	Excluded
1 Finishes to walls **Definition:** Applied finishes to internal wall surfaces, including specialist wall finishes for sports, public amenities and the like.	1 Finishes to walls and columns: details to be stated. 2 Picture rails, dado rails and the like: details to be stated. 3 Proprietary impact and bumper guards, protection strips, corner protectors and the like: details to be stated.	m^2 m nr/m	C1 Where components are to be enumerated, the number of components is to be stated. C2 The area measured for each type of wall finish is the surface area of the wall to which the finish is to be applied. No deduction is made for voids (e.g. for door openings, screens or the like). C3 The length of linear components measured is their extreme length, over all obstructions. C4 Painting and decorating of walls to individual rooms within residential units, hotel rooms, student accommodation units and the like may be enumerated (nr). The type of residential unit or room and size (by number of bedrooms) of unit is to be stated. C5 Other cost significant components are to be described and measured by area (m^2), linear measurement (m) or enumerated (nr) separately, as appropriate.	1 In-situ coatings applied to walls (e.g. plaster, render and roughcast). 2 Sprayed monolithic coatings to columns and walls (i.e. to provide fire protection, thermal insulation, condensation control, and acoustic control). 3 Plasterboard or other sheet linings, including fixing systems, joint reinforcing scrim, plaster skim coats, and the like. 4 Ceramic wall tiling. 5 Decorative sheet coverings, including lining paper, decorative paper, vinyl and plastics wall covering and textile wall covering. 6 Painting and decorating. 7 Picture rails, dado rails and the like. 8 Proprietary impact and bumper guards, protection strips, corner protectors and the like. 9 Insulation which provides a wall finish. 10 Applied finishes to columns.	1 Fire protective coatings and paint systems to structural steel frames (included in *sub-element* 2.1.1: Steel frames). 2 Self finished surfaces (e.g. fair faced blockwork walls, facing bricks, pre-finished partitions and the like – (included in *element* 1.3: Basement retaining walls; *element* 2.5: External walls or *element* 2.7: Internal walls and partitions, as appropriate). 3 Applied finishes to external face of external walls (included in *element* 2.5: External walls, where appropriate). 4 Structural screeds (included in *sub-element* 1.4.1: Ground floor slab/bed and suspended floor construction or *element* 2.2: Upper floors, as appropriate).

Sub-element	Component	Unit	Measurement rules for components	Included	Excluded
			C6 Descriptions shall include the amount of any PC Sum included in the unit rates applied to the item. C7 Curved work is to be described and identified separately. C8 Work to existing buildings is to be described and identified separately.	11 Wall finishes to staircase areas/stairwells. 12 Specialist wall finishes. 13 Sundry items. 14 Where works are to be carried out by a *subcontractor, subcontractor's preliminaries*, design fees, risk allowance, overheads and profit.	

Element 3.2: Floor finishes

Sub-element	Component	Unit	Measurement rules for components	Included	Excluded
1 Finishes to floors **Definition:** Applied finishes to floor surfaces. Including specialist floors to sports facilities, public amenities and the like.	1 Finishes to floors: details to be stated.	m²	C1 Where components are to be enumerated, the number of components is to be stated.	1 Non-structural screeds, including under screed damp-proof membranes.	1 Fire protective coatings and paint systems to structural steel frames (included in *sub-element* 2.1.1: Steel frames).
	2 Specialist flooring systems: details to be stated.	m²	C2 The length of linear components measured is their extreme length, over all obstructions.	2 Latex screeds (i.e. levelling screeds).	2 Structural screeds (included in *sub-element* 1.4.1: Ground floor slab/bed and suspended floor construction or *element* 2.2: Upper floors, as appropriate).
	3 Skirtings and the like: details to be stated.	m	C3 The area measured for each type of floor finish is the surface area of the floor to which the finish is to be applied.	3 Chemical surface hardeners and sealers applied to screeds.	3 Finishes to stair treads and risers (included in *sub-element* 2.4.2: Stair/ramp finishes).
	4 Mat wells and mats: details to be stated.	nr	C4 The area measured for finishings to swimming pool tanks is the area of the swimming pool on plan, measured to the internal face of the swimming pool walls.	4 Floating floors. 5 Resin-bonded resilient layers.	4 Finishes to floor surfaces integral with the floor construction, e.g. timber board flooring, timber strip/board fine flooring (included in *sub-element* 1.4.1: Ground floor slab/bed and suspended floor construction or *element* 2.2: Upper floors, as appropriate).
	5 Finishes to swimming pool tanks, including tank linings: details to be stated.	m²	C5 Other cost significant components are to be described and measured by area (m²), linear measurement (m) or enumerated (nr) separately, as appropriate.	6 In-situ floor finishes (e.g. granolithic and terrazzo). 7 Tiled floor finishes (e.g. stone, quarry, ceramic and mosaic tiles). 8 Wood block flooring, composition block flooring, parquet flooring and the like.	5 Floor coverings and skirtings which form an integral part of a proprietary raised access floor system (included in *sub-element* 3.2.2: Raised access floors).
	6 Line markings: details to be stated.	m	C6 Descriptions shall include the amount of any PC Sum included in the unit rates applied to the item. C7 Curved work is to be described and identified separately.	9 Proprietary thin tiled and strip flooring, blockwood flooring and the like. 10 Floor painting and sealing.	
	7 Numeral and symbols: details to be stated.	nr	C8 Work to existing buildings is to be described and identified separately.	11 Edge fixed carpeting, including underlay, rods, grippers, edgings, and cover and threshold strips.	

Sub-element	Component	Unit	Measurement rules for components	Included	Excluded
				12 Fixed flexible and semi-flexible tile and sheet coverings (e.g. carpet, vinyl, rubber, PVC, thermoplastic, cork, linoleum and antistatic flooring). 13 Timber sprung floors to sports halls, squash courts and the like. 14 Specialist floor covering systems. 15 Finishes to swimming pool tanks, including tank linings. 16 Floor finishes to internal and external balconies. 17 Skirtings. 18 Mat wells and mats. 19 Line markings, numerals, letters, symbols and the like (e.g. surface markings to denote car park spaces in basement car park). 20 Sundry items. 21 Where works are to be carried out by a *subcontractor, subcontractor's preliminaries*, design fees, risk allowance, overheads and profit.	
2 Raised access floors **Definition:** Platform floors or dry construction, raised above the structural floor to create space for the distribution of services.	1 Raised access floor systems: details to be stated. 2 Skirtings and the like: details to be stated.	m² m	C1 The area measured for each type of raised access floor system is the surface area of the floor to which the finish is to be applied. C2 The length of linear components measured is their extreme length, over all obstructions. C3 Other cost significant components are to be described and measured by area (m²), linear measurement (m) or enumerated (nr) separately, as appropriate. C4 Descriptions shall include the amount of any PC Sum included in the unit rates applied to the item. C5 Curved work is to be described and identified separately. C6 Work to existing buildings is to be described and identified separately.	1 Proprietary raised access floor systems, including adjustable pedestals/supports, floor panels, ventilation and access panels, cavity fire barriers, air plenum barriers, outlet boxes and trunking, skirtings/edge trims which form part of the proprietary system, risers and nosings at changes of level, adhesives, bearing pads and shims. 2 Floor coverings/finishes (i.e. where factory bonded or mechanically fixed on site). 3 Sundry items. 4 Where works are to be carried out by a *subcontractor, subcontractor's preliminaries*, design fees, risk allowance, overheads and profit.	1 Floating floors (included in *sub-element* 3.2.1: Finishes to floors). 2 Floor covering, skirtings and the like, which are not an integral part of the raised access floor system (included in *sub-element* 3.2.1: Finishes to floors).

Element 3.3: Ceiling finishes

Sub-element	Component	Unit	Measurement rules for components	Included	Excluded
1 Finishes to ceilings **Definition:** Applied finishes to ceiling surfaces, including specialist ceiling finishes to sports facilities, public amenities and the like.	1 Finishes to ceilings: details to be stated.	m²	C1 The area measured for each type of ceiling finish is the surface area of the ceiling/soffit to which the finish is to be applied.	1 Linings to ceilings (e.g. dry lined plasterboard ceilings, pre-finished sheets, timber boarding and the like).	1 False ceilings (included in *sub-element* 3.3.2: False ceilings).
	2 Cornices, covings and the like: details to be stated.	m	C2 The length of linear components measured is their extreme length, over all obstructions.	2 Linings to sides and soffits of beams, bulkheads and the like.	2 Applied finishes to false ceilings (included in *sub-element* 3.3.2: False ceilings).
			C4 Painting and decorating of ceilings to individual rooms within residential units, hotel rooms, student accommodation units and the like may be enumerated (nr). The type of residential unit or room and size (by number of bedrooms) of unit is to be stated.	3 In-situ coatings applied to ceilings (e.g. plaster skim coat, render, roughcast, and specialist coatings).	3 Demountable suspending ceilings (included in *sub-element* 3.3.3: Demountable suspended ceilings).
			C5 Other cost significant components are to be described and measured by area (m²), linear measurement (m) or enumerated (nr) separately, as appropriate.	4 Sprayed monolithic coatings to beams and ceilings (i.e. to provide fire protection, thermal insulation, condensation control, and acoustic control).	4 Finishes to soffits of staircases, including soffits of landings between floors (included in *sub-element* 2.4.2: Stair/ramp finishes).
			C6 Descriptions shall include the amount of any PC Sum included in the unit rates applied to the item.	5 Painting and decorating to ceilings.	5 Fire protective coatings and paint systems to structural steel frames (included in *sub-element* 2.1.1: Steel frames).
			C7 Curved work is to be described and identified separately.	6 Cornices, covings and the like.	6 Applied finishes to external soffits (included in *sub-element* 2.5.4: External soffits).
			C8 Work to existing buildings is to be described and identified separately.	7 Specialist ceiling finishes.	
				8 Sundry items.	
				9 Where works are to be carried out by a *subcontractor*, *subcontractor's preliminaries*, design fees, risk allowance, overheads and profit.	

Sub-element	Component	Unit	Measurement rules for components	Included	Excluded
2 False ceilings **Definition:** False ceilings comprising soffit linings on battens and the like fixed direct to underside of slabs, not demountable, including specialist false ceilings to sports facilities, public amenities, and the like.	1 False ceilings: details to be stated. 2 Cornices, covings and the like: details to be stated. 3 Access hatches and the like: details to be stated.	m² m nr	C1 The area measured for each type of false ceiling is the surface area of the ceiling/soffit to which the finish is to be applied. C2 The length of linear components measured is their extreme length, over all obstructions. C3 Painting and decorating of walls to individual rooms within residential units, hotel rooms, student accommodation units and the like may be enumerated (nr). The type of residential unit or room and size (by number of bedrooms) of unit is to be stated. C4 Other cost significant components are to be described and measured by area (m²), linear measurement (m) or enumerated (nr) separately, as appropriate. C5 Descriptions shall include the amount of any PC Sum included in the unit rates applied to the item. C6 Curved work is to be described and identified separately. C7 Work to existing buildings is to be described and identified separately.	1 In-situ/board ceilings, including soffit linings, battens, support framework or suspension system, fixed direct to underside of upper floor construction. 2 Insulation; fixed direct to underside of upper floor construction or laid on false ceiling. 3 In-situ coatings applied to false ceilings (e.g. plaster skim coats, render, roughcast, and specialist coatings). 4 Painting and decorating to false ceilings. 5 Cornices, covings and the like. 6 Shadow gaps and the like, including painting. 7 Access hatches and the like in false ceilings. 8 Sundry items. 9 Where works are to be carried out by a *subcontractor, subcontractor's preliminaries*, design fees, risk allowance, overheads and profit.	1 Demountable suspending ceilings (included in *sub-element* 3.3.3: Demountable suspended ceilings). 2 Finishes to soffits of staircases, including soffits of landings between floors (included in *sub-element* 2.4.2: Stair/ramp finishes). 3 Fire protective coatings and paint systems to structural steel frames (included in *sub-element* 2.1.1: Steel frames). 4 False ceilings to external soffits (included in *sub-element* 2.5.4: External soffits).

Sub-element	Component	Unit	Measurement rules for components	Included	Excluded
3 Demountable suspended ceilings **Definition:** False ceilings of dry construction comprising a membrane of tiles, panels and trays supported by exposed or concealed suspended grids. Including specialist false ceilings to sports facilities, public amenities and the like.	1 Demountable suspended ceilings: details to be stated. 2 Shadow gaps and the like: details to be stated. 3 Access hatches and the like: details to be stated.	m² m nr	C1 The area measured for each type of demountable suspended ceiling is the surface area of the ceiling/soffit to which the finish is to be applied. C2 The length of linear components measured is their extreme length, over all obstructions. C3 Other cost significant components are to be described and measured by area (m²), linear measurement (m) or enumerated (nr) separately, as appropriate. C4 Descriptions shall include the amount of any PC Sum included in the unit rates applied to the item. C5 Curved work is to be described and identified separately. C6 Work to existing buildings is to be described and identified separately.	1 Proprietary suspended ceiling systems, including suspension systems. 2 Integrated ceiling systems, including suspension systems. 3 Acoustic suspended ceiling systems, including suspension systems. 4 Specialist suspended ceiling systems, including suspension systems. 5 Insulation; fixed direct to underside of upper floor construction or laid on suspended ceiling system. 6 Shadow gaps and the like, including painting. 7 Access hatches in suspended ceilings and the like. 8 Sundry items. 9 Where works are to be carried out by a *subcontractor, subcontractor's preliminaries*, design fees, risk allowance, overheads and profit.	1 False ceilings (included in *sub-element* 3.3.2: False ceilings). 2 Finishes to soffits of staircases, including soffits of landings between floors (included in *sub-element* 2.4.2: Stair/ramp finishes). 3 Fire protective coatings and paint systems to structural steel frames (included in *sub-element* 2.1.1: Steel frames). 4 Demountable suspended ceilings to external soffits (included in *sub-element* 2.5.4: External soffits).

Group element 4: Fittings, furnishings and equipment

Group element 4 comprises the following elements:

4.1 General fittings, furnishings and equipment

4.2 Special fittings, furnishings and equipment

4.3 Internal planting

4.4 Bird and vermin control

Element 4.1: General fittings, furnishings and equipment

Sub-element	Component	Unit	Measurement rules for components	Included	Excluded
1 General fittings, furnishings and equipment **Definition:** Furnishings, fittings and equipment fixed to the building fabric or provided loose within the building.	1 Fittings: details to be stated.	nr	C1 Where components are to be enumerated, the number of components is to be stated.	1 Counters, counters, desks, benches and worktops.	1 Special purpose fittings, furnishings and equipment (included in *sub-element 4.2.1*: Special purpose fittings, furnishings and equipment).
	2 Furnishings: details to be stated.	nr	C2 Descriptions shall include the amount of any PC Sum included in the unit rates applied to the item.	2 Mirrors, which are not an integral part of wall finishes, furnishings, fittings and equipment.	2 Domestic Kitchen fittings and equipment (included in *sub-element 4.1.2*: Domestic kitchen fittings and equipment).
	3 Equipment: details to be stated.	nr	C3 Work to existing buildings is to be described and identified separately.	3 Curtains, curtain track, rails, pelmets and the like.	3 Mirrors, which are an integral part of wall finishes, e.g. wall tiling (included in *sub-element 3.1.1*: Finishes to walls).
				4 Blinds and blind boxes which are not an integral part of the window system.	4 External blinds, shutters and like (included in *sub-element 2.6.1*: External windows).
				5 Fire place surrounds and hearths.	5 Integral blinds to windows and internal partitions (included in *sub-element 2.6.1*: External windows or *sub-element 2.7.1*: Walls and partitions).
				6 Wall hangings.	
				7 Loose carpets.	
				8 Storage racks, shelves, shelving support systems and the like.	
				9 Tables and chairs.	

Sub-element	Component	Unit	Measurement rules for components	Included	Excluded
				10 Fitted seating, upholstery. 11 Bedroom furniture, including beds, divans, wardrobes, dressers, vanity units, cupboards, cabinets, drawer units and the like. 12 Bathroom furniture, including vanity units, cupboards, and the like. 13 Lockers, hat and coat rails and the like. 14 Hand-held fire fighting equipment, including fire extinguishers, fire blankets and the like, and including backboards, fixings, and the like. 15 Bins, wheelie bins, continental bins and the like. 16 Safes, including building into structure. 17 Vacuum cleaners, cleaning equipment. 18 Televisions, hi-fi and computers. 19 Vending machines. 20 Telephone booths and enclosures (internal). 21 Other general purpose fittings and furnishings. 22 Delivery, unpacking, sorting, checking all components, assembling, fixing in position (including all bolts and other fixing devices). 23 Sundry items. 24 Where works are to be carried out by a *subcontractor, subcontractor's preliminaries,* design fees, risk allowance, overheads and profit.	6 Ironmongery to windows and doors (included in *sub-element* 2.6.1: External windows or *element* 2.8: Internal doors, as ap7 Ironmongery to cubicles (included in *sub-element* 2.7.4: Cubicles). 8 Sanitary appliances and fittings (included in *element* 5.1: Sanitary appliances as appropriate). 9 Mat wells and mats (included in *sub-element* 3.2.1: Finishes to floors). 10 General purpose low voltage (LV) power supplies (included in *sub-element* 5.8.2: Power installations).
2 Domestic kitchen fittings and equipment **Definition:** Domestic kitchen units and equipment of all kinds.	1 Kitchen units: details to be stated. 2 Kitchen appliances: details to be stated. 3 Waste bins, towel rails, storage racks and other accessories: details to be stated.	nr nr nr	C1 Where components are to be enumerated, the number of components is to be stated. C2 Descriptions shall include the amount of any PC Sum included in the unit rates applied to the item. C3 Work to existing buildings is to be described and identified separately.	1 Kitchen units, including base units, drawer units, worktops, cupboards and the like. 2 Sinks, taps, waste fittings, waste disposal units where supplied as part of the kitchen fitting installation. 3 Ovens, cookers, hobs, grill, microwaves and the like. 4 Refrigerators, freezers and the like.	1 Catering equipment (included in *element* 5.2: Services equipment). 2 Sinks not supplied as part of the kitchen fitting installation (*element* 5.2: Services equipment). 3 General purpose low voltage (LV) power supplies (included in *sub-element* 5.8.2: Power installations).

Sub-element	Component	Unit	Measurement rules for components	Included	Excluded
				5 Dishwashers. 6 Clothes washing machines, clothes dryers, ironing cabinets and the like. 7 Waste bins, towel rails, storage racks and other accessories. 8 Kitchen equipment suites comprising any combination of the foregoing. 9 Other kitchen fittings and equipment. 10 Delivery, unpacking, sorting, checking all components, assembling, fixing in position (including all bolts and other fixing devices). 11 Sundry items. 12 Where works are to be carried out by a *subcontractor, subcontractor's preliminaries, design fees, risk allowance, overheads and profit.*	
3 Signs/notices **Definition:** Directories, notice boards, letters, signs, plaques, symbols and emblems of all kinds for identification and directional purposes within or attached to the building.	1 Component: details to be stated.	nr	C1 Where components are to be enumerated, the number of components is to be stated. C2 Descriptions shall include the amount of any PC Sum included in the unit rates applied to the item. C3 Work to existing buildings is to be described and identified separately.	1 Directional signboards. 2 Notice boards, white boards and the like. 3 Sign writing. 4 Shop front lettering, emblems and symbols. 5 Door or floor numbering or lettering. 6 Nameplates, plaques and identification symbols. 7 Lettering, emblems and other identification/directional symbols carved into stone. 8 Delivery, unpacking, sorting, checking all components, assembling, fixing in position (including all bolts and other fixing devices). 9 Sundry items. 10 Where works are to be carried out by a *subcontractor, subcontractor's preliminaries, design fees, risk allowance, overheads and profit.*	1 Illuminated display signs, lettering, emblems and symbols for information purposes, advertising and the like (included in *sub-element* 5.8.5: Specialist lighting installations). 2 Identification labelling and colour coding of services installations and systems (included in *element* 5.14: Builder's work in connection with services).

Sub-element	Component	Unit	Measurement rules for components	Included	Excluded
4 Works of art **Definition:** Objects d'art and other ornamental and decorative features within or attached to the building.	1 Objects d'art and other ornamental features: details to be stated. 2 Decorative features and panels: details to be stated.	nr nr	C1 Where components are to be enumerated, the number of components is to be stated. C2 Descriptions shall include the amount of any PC Sum included in the unit rates applied to the item. C3 Work to existing buildings is to be described and identified separately.	1 Objects d'art and other ornamental features. 2 Decorative features, including panels. 3 Fish tanks, including fish tanks set into internal walls and partitions. 4 Delivery, unpacking, sorting, checking all components, assembling, fixing in position (including all bolts and other fixing devices). 5 Sundry items. 6 Where works are to be carried out by a *subcontractor, subcontractor's preliminaries,* design fees, risk allowance, overheads and profit.	1 Water features, including fountains and waterfalls (included in *sub-element* 5.13.4: Water features).
5 Equipment **Definition:** Non-mechanical and non-electrical equipment for use within or to enter the building.	1 Equipment: details to be stated. 2 Removable ladders and the like: details to be stated.	nr nr	C1 Where components are to be enumerated, the number of components is to be stated. C2 Descriptions shall include the amount of any PC Sum included in the unit rates applied to the item. C3 Work to existing buildings is to be described and identified separately.	1 Removable disabled access equipment. 2 Removable ladders and the like. 3 Other non-mechanical and non-electrical equipment. 4 Delivery, unpacking, sorting, checking all components, assembling, fixing in position (including all bolts and other fixing devices). 5 Sundry items. 6 Where works are to be carried out by a *subcontractor, subcontractor's preliminaries,* design fees, risk allowance, overheads and profit.	1 Fixed access and escape ladders, loft ladders and the like (included in *sub-element* 2.4.4: Ladders/chutes/slides).

Element 4.2: Special fittings, furnishings and equipment

Sub-element	Component	Unit	Measurement rules for components	Included	Excluded
1 Special purpose fittings, furnishings and equipment **Definition:** Furnishings, fittings and equipment non-mechanical or non-electrical equipment fixed to the building fabric or provided loose within the building. 'Special' in the sense that they are designed for the particular purpose(s) of the building and are likely to be obtained from a specialist supplier or specialist contractor for use within the building.	1 Fittings, furnishings and equipment: details to be stated.	nr	C1 Where components are to be enumerated, the number of components is to be stated. C2 Descriptions shall include the amount of any PC Sum included in the unit rates applied to the item. C3 Work to existing buildings is to be described and identified separately.	1 Furnishings, fittings and equipment designed distinctly for a particular type of building, such as: – hospitals, dentist, medical, welfare and animal welfare buildings – entertainment buildings, community centres and clubs, including bars – sports buildings, swimming pools, marinas and stadia – religious and funerary buildings, including seating – educational buildings, including workbenches, blackboards and gymnasia equipment – scientific research buildings, including laboratory workbenches – special residential buildings, hotels and elderly care homes – rail road, water and air transport buildings and terminals – agricultural, fishing and forestry buildings – communications, power supply, mineral supply and water supply buildings – laundry – factories, industrial buildings for food, drink, chemicals, engineering, textiles and the like – shops, showrooms, stores, shopping centres and warehouses – defence, police, prison and fire service buildings – restaurants, snack bars and public houses – libraries, record offices, museums, galleries and zoos.	1 General purpose fittings, furnishings and equipment (included in sub-element 4.1.1: General fittings, furnishings and equipment). 2 Domestic kitchen fittings and equipment (included in sub-element 4.1.2: Domestic kitchen fittings and equipment). 3 Mechanical and electrical services equipment, (included in sub-element 5.2.1: Services equipment). 4 Refuse disposal equipment, incinerators included in element 5.3.3: Refuse disposal, as appropriate).

Sub-element	Component	Unit	Measurement rules for components	Included	Excluded
				2 Other special purpose fittings, furnishings and equipment.	
				3 Delivery, unpacking, sorting, checking all components, assembling, fixing in position (including all bolts and other fixing devices).	
				4 Sundry items.	
				5 Where works are to be carried out by a *subcontractor, subcontractor's preliminaries*, design fees, risk allowance, overheads and profit.	

Element 4.3: Internal planting

Sub-element	Component	Unit	Measurement rules for components	Included	Excluded
1 Internal planting **Definition:** Natural and artificial planting in internal environments.	1 Plant and shrub beds: details to be stated. 2 Trees: details to be stated.	nr/m/m² nr	C1 Where components are to be enumerated, the number of components is to be stated. C2 The area measured is the surface area of planting. C3 Where measured linear; the length measured is the extreme length, over all obstructions. C4 Other cost significant components to be described and measured by area (m²), linear measurement (m) or enumerated (nr) separately, as appropriate. C5 Descriptions shall include the amount of any PC Sum included in the unit rates applied to the item. C6 Work to existing buildings is to be described and identified separately.	1 Internal prefabricated plant and tree containers, including drainage layers, separation layers, capillary matting and wicks, compost, hydro-culture supporting medium and nutrients. 2 Planting container grown plants. 3 Planting shrubs. 4 Planting trees. 5 Plant to containers which are an integral part of the building fabric, including drainage layers, separation layers, capillary matting and wicks, compost, hydro-culture supporting medium and nutrients. 6 Watering, feeding and maintenance during the defects liability period (or period for rectifying defects, or the maintenance period, as appropriate). 7 Replacement planting.	1 Plant containers which are an integral part of the building fabric – construction only (included in *element* 1.3: Basement Retaining Walls; *element* 2.5: External walls or *element* 2.7: Internal walls and partitions, as appropriate). 2 Green roofs and roof gardens, including protection layer, drainage layer, filter membranes and growing medium (included in *sub-element* 2.3.2: Roof coverings). 3 Planting to green roofs/roof gardens (included in *sub-element* 2.3.2: Roof coverings).

Sub-element	Component	Unit	Measurement rules for components	Included	Excluded
				8 Artificial plants, preserved plants and the like, including fixing medium and covering medium for artificial plants. 9 Sundry items. 10 Where works are to be carried out by a *subcontractor, subcontractor's preliminaries*, design fees, risk allowance, overheads and profit.	

Element 4.4: Bird and vermin control

Sub-element	Component	Unit	Measurement rules for components	Included	Excluded
1 Bird and vermin control **Definition:** Installations and equipment to repel, trap or otherwise control birds or vermin which may be a nuisance or danger to health.	1 Wires, nets, traps and the like: details to be stated.	nr	C1 Where components are to be enumerated, the number of components is to be stated. C2 The area measured is the surface area to which the coating is to be applied. C3 Other cost significant components are to be described and measured by area (m²), linear measurement (m) or enumerated (nr) separately, as appropriate. C4 Work to existing buildings is to be described and identified separately.	1 Wires, nets, traps and the like. 2 Electronic and sonic systems. 3 Bird repellent coatings and the like.	
	2 Electronic and sonic system: details to be stated.	nr			
	3 Bird repellent coatings: details to be stated.	m²			

Group element 5: Services

Group element 5 comprises the following elements:

5.1 Sanitary appliances

5.2 Services equipment

5.3 Disposal installations

5.4 Water installations

5.5 Heat source

5.6 Space heating and air conditioning

5.7 Ventilation systems

5.8 Electrical installations

5.9 Gas and other fuel installations

5.10 Lift and conveyor installations

5.11 Fire and lightning protection

5.12 Communication, security and control systems

5.13 Specialist installations

5.14 Builder's work in connection with services

5.15 Testing and commissioning of services

Element 5.1: Sanitary appliances

Sub-element	Component	Unit	Measurement rules for components	Included	Excluded
1 Sanitary appliances **Definition:** Appliances for health, hygiene and personal washing, together with their accessories.	1 Sanitary appliance: details to be stated.	nr	C1 Where components are to be enumerated, the number of components is to be stated. C2 Work to existing buildings is to be described and identified separately.	1 WC pans and cisterns, WC suites, slop hoppers, urinals and cisterns. 2 Sinks, including sinks not supplied as part of the kitchen fitting installation and catering sinks not supplied as part of the catering equipment installation. 3 Wash basins, hand rinse basins, wash fountains. 4 Bidets. 5 Baths, including bath panels and trims. 6 Jacuzzis. 7 Shower trays. 8 Drinking fountains. 9 Taps and waste fittings to the appliances. 10 Saunas, sauna equipment. 11 Sundry items. 12 Where works are to be carried out by a subcontractor, subcontractor's preliminaries, design fees, risk allowance, overheads and profit.	1 Sanitary fittings (included in sub-element 5.1.3: Sanitary fittings). 2 Sinks included with domestic kitchen fittings (included in sub-element 4.1.2: Domestic kitchen fittings and equipment). 3 Sinks included with catering equipment (included in sub-element 5.2.1: Services equipment). 4 Waste pipes, fittings and traps (included in sub-element 5.3.1: Foul drainage above ground). 5 Cold water and hot water distribution (included in sub-element 5.4.2: Cold water distribution or sub-element 5.4.3: Hot water distribution). 6 Instantaneous water heaters, including shower heaters, and storage water heaters (included in sub-element 5.4.4: Local hot water distribution). 7 Heated towel rails, where an integral part of a heating system (included in sub-element 5.6.1: Central heating). 8 Bathroom furniture, including vanity units, cupboards, and the like (included in sub-element 4.1.1: General fittings, furnishings and equipment). 9 Builder's work in connection with services (included in element 5.14: Builder's work in connection with services). 10 Testing and commissioning of services (included in element 5.15: Testing and commissioning of services).

Sub-element	Component	Unit	Measurement rules for components	Included	Excluded
2 Pods **Definition:** Bathroom, toilet and shower pods supplied as completed units manufactured off-site.	1 Bathroom pods: details to be stated. 2 Toilet pods: details to be stated. 3 Shower room pods: details to be stated.	nr nr nr	C1 Where components are to be enumerated, the number of components is to be stated. C2 Work to existing buildings is to be described and identified separately.	1 Pods complete, including structural framework; floor, wall and ceiling linings; applied finishes; sanitary appliances; all fixtures, furnishings and equipment; and all mechanical and electrical services within pod. 2 Bathroom pods. 3 Toilet pods. 4 Shower room pods. 5 All sundry items. 6 Where works are to be carried out by a subcontractor, subcontractor's preliminaries, design fees, risk allowance, overheads and profit.	1 Cold water and hot water distribution feeding pod (included in sub-element 5.4.2: Cold water distribution or sub-element 5.4.2: Hot water distribution). 2 Foul drainage from pod (included in sub-element 5.3.1: Foul drainage above ground). 3 General purpose low voltage (LV) power supplies to pod (included in sub-element 5.8.2: Power installations). 4 Fire resistant stopping, including fire sleeves installed on site (included in element 5.14: Builder's work in connection with services). 5 Builder's work in connection with services (included in element 5.14: Builder's work in connection with services). 6 Testing and commissioning of services (included in element 5.15: Testing and commissioning of services).
3 Sanitary fittings **Definition:** Bathroom, toilet and shower fittings	1 Fittings: details to be stated.	nr	C1 Where components are to be enumerated, the number of components is to be stated. C2 Work to existing buildings is to be described and identified separately.	1 Shower cubicles. 2 Bath/shower curtain rails, screens and the like. 3 Grab/support rails. 4 Towel rails and holders not connected to a heating or hot water supply installation. 5 Hand dryers, including final connection to services. 6 Paper towel dispensers; toilet paper holders; waste bins, soap dispensers and holders. 7 Sanitary incinerators and sanitary macerators. 8 Other sanitary fittings. 9 All sundry items. 10 Where works are to be carried out by a subcontractor, subcontractor's preliminaries, design fees, risk allowance, overheads and profit.	

Element 5.2: Services equipment

Sub-element	Component	Unit	Measurement rules for components	Included	Excluded
1 Services equipment **Definition:** Catering equipment designed for use in provision of food and drink on a communal or commercial scale.	1 Services equipment: details to be stated.	nr	C1 Where components are to be enumerated, the number of components is to be stated. C2 Work to existing buildings is to be described and identified separately.	1 Catering equipment (designed for use in provision of food and drink on a communal or commercial scale). 2 Sinks supplied as an integral part of catering equipment. 3 Food storage equipment. 4 Other free standing or fixed mechanical and electrical equipment to: – hospitals, dentist, medical, welfare and animal welfare buildings – entertainment buildings, community centres and clubs – sports buildings, swimming pools, marinas and stadia – religious and funerary buildings – educational buildings – scientific research buildings – special residential buildings, hotels and elderly care homes – rail road, water and air transport buildings and terminals – agricultural, fishing and forestry buildings – communications, power supply, mineral supply and water supply buildings – laundry – factories, industrial buildings for food, drink, chemicals, engineering, textiles and the like – shops, showrooms, stores, shopping centres and warehouses – defence, police, prison and fire service buildings – restaurants, snack bars and public houses – libraries, record offices, museums, galleries and zoos.	1 Domestic kitchen equipment (included in *sub-element* 4.1.2: Domestic kitchen fittings and equipment). 2 Sinks, taps, waste fittings, waste disposal units where supplied as part of the kitchen fitting installation (included in *sub-element* 4.1.2: Domestic kitchen fittings and equipment). 3 Sanitary appliances (included in *sub-element* 5.1.1: Sanitary appliances or *sub-element* 5.1.2: Pods, as appropriate). 4 Sanitary incinerators and sanitary macerators (included in *sub-element* 5.1.3: Sanitary fittings). 5 Refuse chutes, incineration plant and the like installation (included in *sub-element* 5.3.3: Refuse disposal). 6 Cold rooms, including packaged cold rooms, packaged and walk-in freezers (included in *sub-element* 5.13.3: Specialist refrigeration systems). 7 Builder's work in connection with services (included in *element* 5.14: Builder's work in connection with services). 8 Testing and commissioning of services (included in *element* 5.15: Testing and commissioning of services).

Sub-element	Component	Unit	Measurement rules for components	Included	Excluded
				5 All sundry items. 6 Where works are to be carried out by a subcontractor, subcontractor's preliminaries, design fees, risk allowance, overheads and profit.	

Element 5.3: Disposal installations

Sub-element	Component	Unit	Measurement rules for components	Included	Excluded
1 Foul drainage above ground **Definition:** Piped foul water drainage systems from sanitary appliances, sinks, and kitchen appliances to the first underground drain connection.	1 Drainage to sanitary appliance: details to be stated. 2 Drainage to services equipment: details to be stated.	nr nr	C1 Where components are to be enumerated, the number of components is to be stated. C2 Work to existing buildings is to be described and identified separately.	1 Waste pipes and fittings. 2 Discharge stacks and waste pipes. 3 Ventilating stacks and pipes. 4 Traps, access points, rodding eyes, collars and the like. 5 Prefabricated pipeline assemblies. 6 Prefabricated floor channels and gratings, and drains in upper floor construction. 7 All sundry items. 8 Where works are to be carried out by a subcontractor, subcontractor's preliminaries, design fees, risk allowance, overheads and profit.	1 Drainage to balconies (included in sub-element 2.2.6: Drainage to balconies). 2 Rainwater disposal systems from roofs (included in sub-element 2.3.4: Roof drainage). 3 Drainage to external walkways attached to buildings (included in sub-element 2.5.4: Subsidiary walls, balustrades, handrails, railings and proprietary balconies). 4 Drainage from surface of ground floor assembly to first manhole beyond the enclosing walls of the building (included in sub-element 1.4.1: Ground floor slab/bed and suspended floor construction). 5 Floor outlets and prefabricated floor channels and gratings in ground floor construction (included in sub-element 1.4.1: Ground floor slab/bed and suspended floor construction). 6 Internal manholes and the like (included in sub-element 1.4.1: Ground floor slab/bed and suspended floor construction). 7 Drainage from first manhole beyond the enclosing walls of the building (included in sub-element 8.6.1: Surface water and foul water drainage).

Sub-element	Component	Unit	Measurement rules for components	Included	Excluded
					8 Rainwater harvesting systems, including collection pipelines (included in sub-element 5.4.2: Cold water distribution or sub-element 8.7.1: Water mains supply, as appropriate). 9 Grey water systems, including collection pipelines (included in sub-element 5.4.2: Cold water distribution or sub-element 8.7.1: Water mains supply as appropriate). 10 Builder's work in connection with services (included in element 5.14: Builder's work in connection with services). 11 Testing and commissioning of services (included in element 5.15: Testing and commissioning of services).
2 Laboratory and industrial liquid waste drainage **Definition:** Separate piped waste disposal systems where the waste needs special treatment or separate storage before disposal from appliance or equipment to external face of the external wall to the building.	1 Drainage to appliance or equipment: details to be stated.	nr	C1 Where components are to be enumerated, the number of components is to be stated. C2 Work to existing buildings is to be described and identified separately.	1 Pipelines and fittings, including glass drainage. 2 Traps, access points, rodding eyes, collars and the like. 3 Gullies. 4 Connections tanks and the like. 5 Storage tanks and vessels. 6 Settlement tanks. 7 Effluent treatment plant. 8 Dosing equipment. 9 Sterilisation equipment. 10 Supports integral to the storage tanks and vessels, settlement tanks, or the like. 11 Thermal insulation. 12 Connections to equipment. 13 Control components located externally. 14 Monitoring equipment located externally. 15 Painting, anti-corrosion treatments and coating systems to drainage pipelines. 17 Sundry items. 18 Where works are to be carried out by a subcontractor, subcontractor's preliminaries, design fees, risk allowance, overheads and profit.	1 Laboratory and industrial liquid waste drainage from external face of the external wall to the building to the point of disposal (included in sub-element 8.6.3: External laboratory and industrial liquid waste drainage). 2 Builder's work in connection with services (included in element 5.14: Builder's work in connection with services). 3 Testing and commissioning of services (included in element 5.15: Testing and commissioning of services).

Sub-element	Component	Unit	Measurement rules for components	Included	Excluded
3 Refuse disposal **Definition:** Refuse chutes, incineration plant and the like.	1 Refuse disposal installation: details to be stated.	nr	C1 Where components are to be enumerated, the number of components is to be stated. C2 Work to existing buildings is to be described and identified separately.	1 Refuse input devices. 2 Refuse chutes and ducts. 3 Plant for the compacting/macerating of refuse ready for collection. 4 Refuse collection equipment, including bins and continental bins. 5 Incineration plant and ancillaries, including refuse and waste handling equipment, afterburners, proprietary metal chimney and flues, and ash handling equipment. 6 Paper shredders. 7 Safety devices. 8 Painting/anti-corrosive treatments. 9 Final connection to services. 10 All sundry items. 11 Where works are to be carried out by a *subcontractor, subcontractor's preliminaries*, design fees, risk allowance, overheads and profit.	1 Sanitary incinerators and sanitary macerators (included in *sub-element* 5.1.3: Sanitary fittings). 2 Builder's work in connection with services (included in *element* 5.14: Builder's work in connection with services). 3 Testing and commissioning of services (included in *element* 5.15: Testing and commissioning of services).

Element 5.4: Water installations

Sub-element	Component	Unit	Measurement rules for components	Included	Excluded
1 Mains water supply **Definition:** Piped water supply systems from point of entry into building to appliance or equipment.	1 Mains water supply: details, including the number of draw-off points (nr), to be stated.	nr/m²	C1 Where components are to be enumerated, the number of components is to be stated. C2 The area measured is the total gross internal floor area (GIFA) of the building, measured using the rules of measurement for ascertaining the GIFA.	1 Pipelines and pipeline fittings. 2 Valves. 3 Water meters, internal. 4 Rising main to storage tanks. 5 Water meters, where not provided as part of water mains supply installation by the statutory undertaker. 6 Trace heating.	1 Piped water supply systems bringing water from the statutory undertaker's mains to point of entry into building (included in *sub-element* 8.7.1: Water mains supply). 2 Connections to statutory undertaker's water main (included in *sub-element* 8.7.1: Water mains supply).

Sub-element	Component	Unit	Measurement rules for components	Included	Excluded
			C3 Installations to residential units, hotel rooms, student accommodation units and the like may be enumerated (nr). The type of residential unit or room and size (by number of bedrooms) of unit is to be stated. C4 Work to existing buildings is to be described and identified separately.	7 Thermal insulation. 8 Sundry items. 9 Where works are to be carried out by a *subcontractor, subcontractor's preliminaries,* design fees, risk allowance, overheads and profit.	3 Storage tanks (included in *sub-element* 5.4.2: Cold water distribution). 4 Water meters, where provided as part of water mains supply by the statutory undertaker (included in *sub-element* 8.7.1: Water mains supply). 5 Builder's work in connection with services (included in *element* 5.14: Builder's work in connection with services). 6 Testing and commissioning of services (included in *element* 5.15: Testing and commissioning of services).
2 Cold water distribution **Definition:** Piped water supply systems to distribute cold water from point of storage to user point.	1 Cold water distribution: details, including the number of draw-off points (nr), to be stated.	nr/m²	C1 Where components are to be enumerated, the number of components is to be stated. C2 The area measured is the area serviced by the system (i.e. the area of the rooms and circulation spaces that are served by the system, which is not necessarily the total gross internal floor area (GIFA) of the building). The area serviced is measured using the rules of measurement for ascertaining the GIFA. C3 Installations to residential units, hotel rooms, student accommodation units and the like may be enumerated (nr). The type of residential unit or room and size (by number of bedrooms) of unit is to be stated. C4 Work to existing buildings is to be described and identified separately.	1 Cold water distribution pipelines to sanitary appliances, sinks, equipment and the like, including fittings. 2 Valves. 3 Taps, where not part of a sanitary appliance or services equipment. 4 Pumps. 5 Pressurisation expansion units. 6 Pressure booster sets. 7 Water storage tanks, and cisterns. 8 Trace heating. 9 Instrumentation and control components to cold water distribution systems. 10 Thermal insulation. 11 Rainwater harvesting systems (internal), including collection pipelines. 12 Grey water collection pipe systems (internal), including collection pipelines. 13 Sundry items. 14 Where works are to be carried out by a *subcontractor, subcontractor's preliminaries,* design fees, risk allowance, overheads and profit.	1 Taps to sanitary appliances and domestic kitchen sinks (included in *sub-element* 5.1.1: Sanitary appliances or 4.1.2: Domestic kitchen fittings and equipment, as appropriate). 2 Taps and valves to services equipment (included in *sub-element* 5.2.1: Services equipment). 3 Water tanks (i.e. header tanks), including cold water distribution to heat source (included in *sub-element* 5.5.1: Heat source). 4 Building management systems and other control systems (included in *sub-element* 5.12.3: Central control/building management systems (BMS)). 5 Builder's work in connection with services (included in *element* 5.14: Builder's work in connection with services). 6 Testing and commissioning of services (included in *element* 5.15: Testing and commissioning of services).

Sub-element	Component	Unit	Measurement rules for components	Included	Excluded
3 Hot water distribution **Definition:** Piped water supply systems to distribute hot water to sanitary appliances, sinks, equipment and other appliances and to distribute mixed water to water heaters and equipment.	1 Hot water distribution: details, including the number of draw-off points (nr). to be stated.	nr/m²	C1 Where components are to be enumerated, the number of components is to be stated. C2 The area measured is the area serviced by the system (i.e. the area of the rooms and circulation spaces that are served by the system, which is not necessarily the total gross internal floor area (GIFA) of the building). The area serviced is measured using the rules of measurement for ascertaining the GIFA. C3 Installations to residential units, hotel rooms, student accommodation units and the like may be enumerated (nr). The type of residential unit or room and size (by number of bedrooms) of unit is to be stated. C4 Work to existing buildings is to be described and identified separately.	1 Hot water distribution pipelines to sanitary appliances, sinks, equipment and the like, including fittings. 2 Valves. 3 Taps, where not part of a sanitary appliance or services equipment. 4 Pumps. 5 Heat exchangers. 6 Storage cylinders, calorifiers. 7 Trace heating. 8 Hot water storage vessels and expansion vessels. 9 Immersion heaters. 10 Insulated combination units. 11 Water softeners. 12 Instrumentation and control components to hot water distribution systems. 13 Thermal insulation. 14 Sundry items. 15 Where works are to be carried out by a *subcontractor*, *subcontractor's preliminaries*, design fees, risk allowance, overheads and profit.	1 Boilers or other heat sources (included in *sub-element* 5.5.1: Heat source). 2 Taps to sanitary appliances and domestic kitchen sinks (included in *sub-element* 5.1.1: Sanitary appliances or 4.1.2: Domestic kitchen fittings and equipment, as appropriate). 3 Taps and valves to services equipment (included in *sub-element* 5.2.1: Services equipment). 4 Building management systems and other control systems (included in *sub-element* 5.12.3: Central control/building management systems (BMS)). 5 Builder's work in connection with services (included in *element* 5.14: Builder's work in connection with services). 6 Testing and commissioning of services (included in *element* 5.15: Testing and commissioning of services).
4 Local hot water distribution **Definition:** Systems where hot water is generated in the vicinity of the appliance being served.	1 Water heaters: details to be stated.	nr	C1 Where components are to be enumerated, the number of components is to be stated. C2 Work to existing buildings is to be described and identified separately.	1 Instantaneous water heaters (including shower heaters) and storage water heaters, including flue pipes and terminals. 2 Sundry items. 3 Where works are to be carried out by a *subcontractor*, *subcontractor's preliminaries*, design fees, risk allowance, overheads and profit.	1 Builder's work in connection with services (included in *element* 5.14: Builder's work in connection with services). 2 Testing and commissioning of services (included in *element* 5.15: Testing and commissioning of services).

Sub-element	Component	Unit	Measurement rules for components	Included	Excluded
5 Steam and condensate distribution **Definition:** Steam distribution and condensate return pipelines to and from services equipment within the building.	1 Steam and condensate distribution: details, including number of draw-off points (nr), to be stated.	nr/m²	C1 Where components are to be enumerated, the number of components is to be stated. C2 The area measured is the area serviced by the system (i.e. the area of the rooms and circulation spaces that are served by the system, which is not necessarily the total gross internal floor area (GIFA) of the building). The area serviced is measured using the rules of measurement for ascertaining the GIFA. C3 Installations to residential units, hotel rooms, student accommodation units and the like may be enumerated (nr). The type of residential unit or room and size (by number of bedrooms) of unit is to be stated. C4 Work to existing buildings is to be described and identified separately.	1 Steam distribution pipelines to and condensate return pipelines from services equipment, including fittings. 2 Valves, strainers, pressure reducing sets, and the like. 3 Steam reduction stations. 4 Condensate receivers and storage tanks. 5 Condensate pump sets. 6 Steam connection outlets. 7 Taps, where not part of services equipment. 8 Heat exchangers. 9 Storage cylinders, calorifiers. 10 Instrumentation and control components to steam and condensate systems. 11 Thermal insulation. 13 Sundry items. 14 Where works are to be carried out by a *subcontractor, subcontractor's preliminaries,* design fees, risk allowance, overheads and profit.	1 Steam generators or other heat sources (included in *sub-element* 5.5.1: Heat source). 2 Taps and valves to services equipment (included in *sub-element* 5.2.1: Services equipment). 3 Building management systems and other control systems (included in *sub-element* 5.12.3: Central control/building management systems (BMS)). 4 Builder's work in connection with services (included in *element* 5.14: Builder's work in connection with services). 5 Testing and commissioning of services (included in *element* 5.15: Testing and commissioning of services).

Element 5.5: Heat source

Sub-element	Component	Unit	Measurement rules for components	Included	Excluded
1 Heat source **Definition:** A heat source supplying heat to one or more heating systems.	1 Heat source (nr): details, including output of heat source (kW), to be stated.	nr	C1 Where components are to be enumerated, the number of components is to be stated. C2 Work to existing buildings is to be described and identified separately.	1 Biomass fuel boiler plant and ancillary items. 2 Gas/oil fired boiler plant and ancillary items, including burners, blow down facilities and pressurisation plant. 3 Coal fired boiler plant and ancillary items, including burners, blow down facilities, coal distribution equipment, ash handling and storage equipment, grit arrestors and pressurisation plant. 4 Electric boiler plant and ancillaries, including blow down facilities and pressurisation plant.	1 Heat distribution and delivery (included in *element* 5.6: Space heating and air conditioning). 2 Chimneys and flues which are an integral part of the building structure shall be included with the appropriate structural element. 3 Local heat source (included in *sub-element* 5.6.2: Local heating).

Sub-element	Component	Measurement rules for components	Included	Excluded
			5 Packaged steam generators and ancillaries, including blow down facilities and pressurisation plant. 6 Wood pellet boiler plant and ancillary items. 7 Central (combined) heat and power (CHP) boiler plant. 8 Heat pumps (including domestic air to water heat pumps). 9 Ground source heating (GSH), including boreholes and all ancillary components (including closed loop and open loop systems). 10 Water or steam mains, pumps, valves and other equipment from district heating systems. 11 Step down/non-storage calorifiers connected to external heat source. 12 Other heat sources. 13 Water tanks (i.e. header tanks), including cold water distribution to heat source. 14 Vibration isolation mountings. 15 Instrumentation and control components to heat source. 16 Forced draft fans. 17 Gantries. 18 Chimneys and flues, where not part of the building. 19 Forced draft extract. 20 Sundry items. 21 Where works are to be carried out by a *subcontractor*, *subcontractor's preliminaries*, design fees, risk allowance, overheads and profit.	4 Fuel storage (included in *sub-element* 5.9.2: Fuel storage and piped distribution systems or *sub-element* 8.7.7: External fuel storage and piped distribution systems, as appropriate). 5 Photovoltaic tiles, panels and the like (included in *sub-element* 5.8.6: Transformation devices). 6 Wind turbines (included in *sub-element* 5.8.6: Transformation devices). 7 Solar collectors (included in *sub-element* 5.8.6: Transformation devices). 8 Local generation equipment for the production of electrical energy, including emergency and or standby generator plant (included in *sub-element* 5.8.5: Local electricity generation systems). 9 Building management systems and other control systems (included in *sub-element* 5.12.3: Central control/building management systems (BMS)). 10 Builder's work in connection with services (included in *element* 5.14: Builder's work in connection with services). 11 Testing and commissioning of services (included in *element* 5.15: Testing and commissioning of services).

Element 5.6: Space heating and air conditioning

Sub-element	Component	Unit	Measurement rules for components	Included	Excluded
1 Central heating Definition: Systems where heating is generated at a central point and distributed to the spaces and/or locations being treated.	1 Central heating systems: details to be stated.	m²	C1 The area measured is the area serviced by the system (i.e. the area of the rooms and circulation spaces that are served by the system, which is not necessarily the total gross internal floor area (GIFA) of the building). The area serviced is measured using the rules of measurement for ascertaining the GIFA. C2 Where more than one system is employed, the area measured for each system is the area serviced by the system. Areas to be measured using the rules of measurement for ascertaining the GIFA. C3 Installations to residential units, hotel rooms, student accommodation units and the like may be enumerated (nr). The type of residential unit or room and size (by number of bedrooms) of unit is to be stated. C4 Work to existing buildings is to be described and identified separately.	1 Heating systems from, and including everything within, the plant room specifically related to the heating system, excluding the heat source. 2 Heat distribution pipelines from heat source to heat emitter or other equipment. 3 Heat emission units, such as: – radiator systems – radiant panel systems – radiant strip heater systems – natural convectors – fan convectors – unit heaters – radiators – convector heaters – skirting heaters – continuous convectors. 4 In-screed embedded pipelines (i.e. under floor heating). 5 Heated ceiling panels. 6 Warm air heating. 7 Convection systems. 8 Fan assisted convection systems including under-floor systems. 9 Cable heating systems. 10 Plenum air heating system. 11 Off-peak heating system, including storage radiators. 12 Distribution pipelines and pipeline fittings. 13 Heated towel rails, where an integral part of a heating system.	1 Heat source (included in *element* 5.5: Heat source). 2 Electrically operated heaters other than in storage radiator (included in *sub-element* 5.6.2: Local heating). 3 General purpose low voltage (LV) power supplies (included in *sub-element* 5.8.2: Power installations). 4 Building management systems and other control systems (included in *sub-element* 5.12.3: Central control/building management systems (BMS)). 5 Builder's work in connection with services (included in *element* 5.14: Builder's work in connection with services). 6 Testing and commissioning of services (included in *element* 5.15: Testing and commissioning of services).

Sub-element	Component	Unit	Measurement rules for components	Included	Excluded
				14 Valves and fittings. 15 Ductwork. 16 Air handling equipment. 17 Grilles, fans, filters and the like. 18 Cables. 19 Instrumentation and control components to heating systems. 20 Thermal insulation. 21 Sundry items. 22 Where works are to be carried out by a *subcontractor, subcontractor's preliminaries*, design fees, risk allowance, overheads and profit.	
2 Local heating **Definition:** Systems where heating is generated in or adjacent to the space or location to be treated.	1 Heaters: details to be stated.	nr	C1 Where components are to be enumerated, the number of components is to be stated. C2 Installations to residential units, hotel rooms, student accommodation units and the like may be enumerated (nr). The type of residential unit or room and size (by number of bedrooms) of unit is to be stated. C3 Work to existing buildings is to be described and identified separately.	1 Room heaters or fires, with or without boilers. 2 Chimneys and flues, where not part of the building structure (e.g. proprietary chimneys and flue pipes). 3 Instrumentation and control components to heating systems. 4 Sundry items. 5 Where works are to be carried out by a *subcontractor, subcontractor's preliminaries*, design fees, risk allowance, overheads and profit.	1 Chimneys and flues which are an integral part of the structure shall be included with the appropriate structural element. 2 General purpose low voltage (LV) power supplies (included in *sub-element 5.8.2*: Power installations). 3 Building management systems and other control systems (included in *sub-element 5.12.3*: Central control/building management systems (BMS)). 4 Builder's work in connection with services (included in *element 5.14*: Builder's work in connection with services). 5 Testing and commissioning of services (included in *element 5.15*: Testing and commissioning of services).

Sub-element	Component	Unit	Measurement rules for components	Included	Excluded
3 Central cooling **Definition:** Systems where cooling is performed at a central point and distributed to the spaces and/or locations being treated.	1 Central cooling systems: details to be stated.	m²	C1 The area measured is the area serviced by the system (i.e. the area of the rooms and circulation spaces that are served by the system, which is not necessarily the total gross internal floor area (GIFA) of the building). The area serviced is measured using the rules of measurement for ascertaining the GIFA. C2 Where more than one system is employed, the area measured for each system is the area serviced by the system. Areas to be measured using the rules of measurement for ascertaining the GIFA. C3 Work to existing buildings is to be described and identified separately.	1 Chilled beams. 2 Fan coil systems for cooling only. 3 Air based systems – variable air volume (VAV) for cooling only. 4 Variable refrigerant volume (VRV) systems. 5 Chillers and packaged chillers. 6 Central refrigeration plant. 7 Cooling towers. 8 Distribution pipelines and pipeline fittings. 9 Cold and treated water feeds. 10 Valves. 11 Pumps. 12 Distribution ductwork and ductwork fittings and ancillaries, e.g. supports, hangers, access openings and dampers (control, fire and smoke). 13 Grilles, fans, filters and other ancillary components of central cooling systems. 14 Air handling units (AHUs). 15 Emission units, including fan coil units, chilled beam and the like. 16 Instrumentation and control components to central cooling systems. 17 Thermal insulation. 18 Sundry items. 19 Where works are to be carried out by a *subcontractor, subcontractor's preliminaries*, design fees, risk allowance, overheads and profit.	1 General purpose low voltage (LV) power supplies (included in *sub-element 5.8.2*: Power installations). 2 Building management systems and other control systems (included in *sub-element 5.12.3*: Central control/building management systems (BMS)). 3 External cooling towers (included in *sub-element 8.8.2*: Ancillary buildings/structures). 4 Builder's work in connection with services (included in *element 5.14*: Builder's work in connection with services). 5 Testing and commissioning of services (included in *element 5.15*: Testing and commissioning of services).

Sub-element	Component	Unit	Measurement rules for components	Included	Excluded
4 Local cooling **Definition:** Systems where cooling is performed in or adjacent to the space or location to be treated.	1 Cooling units: details to be stated.	nr	C1 Where components are to be enumerated, the number of components is to be stated. C2 Installations to residential units, hotel rooms, student accommodation units and the like may be enumerated (nr). The type of residential unit or room and size (by number of bedrooms) of unit is to be stated. C3 Work to existing buildings is to be described and identified separately.	1 Local cooling units, including those with remote condensers. 2 Distribution pipelines and pipeline fittings. 3 Valves. 4 Distribution ductwork and ductwork fittings and ancillaries, e.g. supports, hangers, access openings and dampers (control, fire and smoke). 5 Grilles, fans, filters and other ancillary components of local cooling systems. 6 Valves and fittings. 7 Instrumentation and control components to local cooling systems. 8 Thermal insulation. 9 Sundry items. 10 Where works are to be carried out by a *subcontractor, subcontractor's preliminaries*, design fees, risk allowance, overheads and profit.	1 General purpose low voltage (LV) power supplies (included in *sub-element* 5.8.2: Power installations). 2 Building management systems and other control systems (included in *sub-element* 5.12.3: Central control/building management systems (BMS)). 3 Builder's work in connection with services (included in *element* 5.14: Builder's work in connection with services). 4 Testing and commissioning of services (included in *element* 5.15: Testing and commissioning of services).
5 Central heating and cooling **Definition:** Combined systems where heating and cooling are performed at a central point and distributed to the spaces and locations being treated.	1 Combined central heating and cooling systems: details to be stated.	m²	C1 The area measured is the area serviced by the system (i.e. the area of the rooms and circulation spaces that are served by the system, which is not necessarily the total gross internal floor area (GIFA) of the building). The area serviced is measured using the rules of measurement for ascertaining the GIFA. C2 Where more than one system is employed, the area measured for each system is the area serviced by the system. Areas to be measured using the rules of measurement for ascertaining the GIFA. C3 Installations to residential units, hotel rooms, student accommodation units and the like may be enumerated (nr). The type of residential unit or room and size (by number of bedrooms) of unit is to be stated.	1 Fan coil systems for heating and cooling. 2 Air based systems – variable air volume (VAV) for heating and cooling. 3 Reverse cycle heat pump systems. 4 Chillers, including vapour compression chillers, absorption chillers (run using low-grade waste heat from other industrial process), solar thermal absorption chillers, and the like. 5 Distribution pipelines and pipeline fittings. 6 Valves. 7 Pumps. 8 Distribution ductwork and ductwork fittings and ancillaries, e.g. supports, hangers, access openings and dampers (control, fire and smoke).	1 General purpose low voltage (LV) power supplies (included in *sub-element* 5.8.2: Power installations). 2 Building management systems and other control systems (included in *sub-element* 5.12.3: Central control/building management systems (BMS)). 3 Builder's work in connection with services (included in *element* 5.14: Builder's work in connection with services). 4 Testing and commissioning of services (included in *element* 5.15: Testing and commissioning of services).

Sub-element	Component	Unit	Measurement rules for components	Included	Excluded
			C4 Work to existing buildings is to be described and identified separately.	9 Grilles, fans, filters and other ancillary components of central heating and cooling systems. 10 Air handling units (AHUs). 11 Emission equipment, including fan coil units and the like. 12 Vibration isolation mountings. 13 Instrumentation and control components to central heating and cooling systems. 14 Thermal insulation. 15 Sundry items. 16 Where works are to be carried out by a *subcontractor*, *subcontractor's preliminaries*, design fees, risk allowance, overheads and profit.	
6 Local heating and cooling **Definition:** Combined systems where heating and cooling are performed in or adjacent to the space to be treated.	1 Local heating and cooling units: details to be stated.	nr	C1 Where components are to be enumerated, the number of components is to be stated. C2 Installations to residential units, hotel rooms, student accommodation units and the like may be enumerated (nr). The type of residential unit or room and size (by number of bedrooms) of unit is to be stated. C3 Work to existing buildings is to be described and identified separately.	1 Local heating and cooling units, including those with remote condensers. 2 Distribution pipelines and pipeline fittings. 3 Valves. 4 Pumps. 5 Distribution ductwork and ductwork fittings and ancillaries, e.g. supports, hangers, access openings and dampers (control, fire and smoke). 6 Grilles, fans, filters and other ancillary components of local heating and cooling systems. 7 Vibration isolation mountings. 8 Instrumentation and control components to local heating and cooling systems. 9 Thermal insulation. 10 Sundry items. 11 Where works are to be carried out by a *subcontractor*, *subcontractor's preliminaries*, design fees, risk allowance, overheads and profit.	1 General purpose low voltage (LV) power supplies (included in *sub-element* 5.8.2: Power installations). 2 Building management systems and other control systems (included in *sub-element* 5.12.3: Central control/building management systems (BMS)). 3 Builder's work in connection with services (included in *element* 5.14: Builder's work in connection with services). 4 Testing and commissioning of services (included in *element* 5.15: Testing and commissioning of services).

Sub-element	Component	Unit	Measurement rules for components	Included	Excluded
7 Central air conditioning **Definition:** Systems where air treatment is performed at a central point and air is distributed to the spaces and locations being treated.	1 Central air conditioning system: details to be stated.	m²	C1 The area measured is the area serviced by the system (i.e. the area of the rooms and circulation spaces that are served by the system, which is not necessarily the total gross internal floor area (GIFA) of the building). The area serviced is measured using the rules of measurement for ascertaining the GIFA. C2 Where more than one system is employed, the area measured for each system is the area serviced by the system. Areas to be measured using the rules of measurement for ascertaining the GIFA. C3 Installations to residential units, hotel rooms, student accommodation units and the like may be enumerated (nr). The type of residential unit or room and size (by number of bedrooms) of unit is to be stated. C4 Work to existing buildings is to be described and identified separately.	1 Plenum air heating systems. 2 VAV (variable air volume) and constant volume air conditioning systems. 3 Dual-duct and induction air conditioning systems. 4 Multi-zone air conditioning systems. 5 Induction air conditioning systems. 6 Hybrid air conditioning systems (i.e. systems based on a combination of a number of other air conditioning systems). 7 Chillers. 8 Air handling units (AHUs). 9 Terminal units/emitters. 10 Distribution pipelines and pipeline fittings. 11 Valves. 12 Pumps. 13 Distribution ductwork and ductwork fittings and ancillaries, e.g. supports, hangers, access openings and dampers (control, fire and smoke). 14 Grilles, fans, filters and other ancillary components of central air conditioning systems. 15 Instrumentation and control components to central air conditioning systems. 16 Thermal insulation. 17 Sundry items. 18 Where works are to be carried out by a *subcontractor, subcontractor's preliminaries*, design fees, risk allowance, overheads and profit.	1 Heat source (included in *element* 5.5: Heat source). 2 Local cooling and air treatment independent of heating systems, e.g. local comfort cooling, included in *sub-element* 5.6.8: Local air conditioning). 3 General purpose low voltage (LV) power supplies (included in *sub-element* 5.8.2: Power installations). 4 Building management systems and other control systems (included in *sub-element* 5.12.3: Central control/building management systems (BMS)). 5 Builder's work in connection with services (included in *element* 5.14: Builder's work in connection with services). 6 Testing and commissioning of services (included in *element* 5.15: Testing and commissioning of services).

Sub-element	Component	Unit	Measurement rules for components	Included	Excluded
8 Local air conditioning **Definition:** Systems where air treatment is performed in or adjacent to the space to be treated.	1 Self-contained air conditioning units: details to be stated.	nr	C1 Where components are to be enumerated, the number of components is to be stated. C2 Installations to residential units, hotel rooms, student accommodation units and the like may be enumerated (nr). The type of residential unit or room and size (by number of bedrooms) of unit is to be stated. C3 Work to existing buildings is to be described and identified separately.	1 Self-contained air conditioning units providing conditioned air to rooms or areas, including units with remote condensers. 2 Separate clean room or other local air conditioning systems requiring air management (e.g. terminal re-heat and terminal heat pump air conditioning systems). 3 Distribution pipelines and pipeline fittings. 4 Valves. 5 Pumps. 6 Distribution ductwork and ductwork fittings and ancillaries (e.g. supports, hangers, access openings and dampers (control, fire and smoke)). 7 Grilles, fans, filters and other ancillary components of local air conditioning systems. 8 Vibration isolation mountings 9 Instrumentation and control components to local air conditioning systems. 10 Thermal insulation. 11 Air curtains (i.e. air movement systems for circulating 'curtain' of tempered air across the dividing space between two areas of differing temperatures). 12 Sundry items. 13 Where works are to be carried out by a *subcontractor, subcontractor's preliminaries, design fees, risk allowance, overheads and profit.*	1 Heat source (included in *element 5.5: Heat source*). 2 General purpose low voltage (LV) power supplies (included in *sub-element 5.8.2: Power installations*). 3 Building management Systems and other control systems (included in *sub-element 5.12.3: Central control/building management systems (BMS)*). 4 Builder's work in connection with services (included in *element 5.14: Builder's work in connection with services*). 5 Testing and commissioning of services (included in *element 5.15: Testing and commissioning of services*).
	2 Other local air conditioning systems: details to be stated.	nr			

Element 5.7: Ventilation systems

Sub-element	Component	Unit	Measurement rules for components	Included	Excluded
1 Central ventilation **Definition:** Air movement systems removing vitiated air from spaces and/or supplying fresh outside air to spaces. No environmental control or air treatment except filtration when required.	1 Central ventilation systems: details to be stated.	m²	C1 The area measured is the area serviced by the system (i.e. the area of the rooms and circulation spaces that are served by the system, which is not necessarily the total gross internal floor area (GIFA) of the building). The area serviced is measured using the rules of measurement for ascertaining the GIFA. C2 Where more than one system is employed, the area measured for each system is the area serviced by the system. Areas to be measured using the rules of measurement for ascertaining the GIFA. C3 Work to existing buildings is to be described and identified separately.	1 Air extract systems. 2 Air supply and extract systems. 3 Extract units/terminal units. 4 Fan units. 5 Distribution ductwork and ductwork fittings and ancillaries, e.g. supports, hangers, access openings and dampers (control, fire and smoke). 6 Grilles, fans, filters and other ancillary components of central ventilation systems. 7 Distribution pipelines and pipeline fittings. 8 Valves. 9 Pumps. 10 Vibration isolation mountings. 11 Instrumentation and control components to central ventilation systems. 12 Sundry items. 13 Where works are to be carried out by a subcontractor, subcontractor's preliminaries, design fees, risk allowance, overheads and profit.	1 General purpose low voltage (LV) power supplies (included in *sub-element* 5.8.2: Power installations). 2 Building management systems and other control systems (included in *sub-element* 5.12.3: Central control/building management systems (BMS)). 3 Builder's work in connection with services (included in *element* 5.14: Builder's work in connection with services). 4 Testing and commissioning of services (included in *element* 5.15: Testing and commissioning of services).

Sub-element	Component	Unit	Measurement rules for components	Included	Excluded
2 Local and special ventilation **Definition:** Local and special air movement systems removing vitiated air from spaces and/or supplying fresh air outside air to spaces. No environmental control or air treatment except filtration when required.	1 Toilet/bathroom ventilation units: details to be stated.	nr	C1 Where components are to be enumerated, the number of components is to be stated. C2 Work to existing buildings is to be described and identified separately.	1 Toilet/bathroom ventilation (air movement systems for removing smells, odours and other unwanted contaminants from, or supplying fresh air to, toilet areas, e.g. packaged toilet extract fans).	1 Kitchen ventilation units where an integral part of a domestic kitchen installation or catering installation (included in *sub-element* 4.1.2: Domestic kitchen fittings and equipment or *sub-element* 5.2.1: Services equipment). 2 General purpose low voltage (LV) power supplies (included in *sub-element* 5.8.2: Power installations). 3 Building management systems and other control systems (included in *sub-element* 5.12.3: Central control/building management systems (BMS)). 4 Builder's work in connection with services (included in *element* 5.14: Builder's work in connection with services). 5 Testing and commissioning of services (included in *element* 5.15: Testing and commissioning of services).
	2 Kitchen ventilation units: details to be stated.	nr		2 Kitchen ventilation (air movement systems for collecting, containing and removing smells, fumes and other unwanted contaminants from, or supplying fresh air to, kitchen areas), including hoods, canopies and grease filters.	
	3 Safety cabinet and fume cupboard extracts: details to be stated.	nr		3 Safety cabinet and fume cupboard extracts (air movement systems for collecting, containing, cleaning and removing smells, fumes and other unwanted contaminants), including safety cabinets and fume cupboard extracts with integral extract.	
	4 Fume extracts: details to be stated.	nr		4 Fume extracts (air movement systems for collecting, containing, cleaning and removing smells, fumes and other unwanted contaminants), including hoods, canopies and valances.	
	5 Dust collection units; details to be stated.	nr		5 Dust collection, including dust and particle extraction or separation equipment, discharge stacks, hoods and collection equipment.	
	6 Anaesthetic gas extracts: details to be stated.	nr		6 Anaesthetic gas extracts (i.e. scavenging systems for the removal of anaesthetic gases).	
	7 Cyclone systems: details to be stated.	nr		7 Cyclone systems.	
	8 Unit extract fans: details to be stated.	nr		8 Unit extract fans.	
	9 Rotating ventilators: details to be stated.	nr		9 Rotating ventilators.	
	10 Roof mounted ventilation units: details to be stated.	nr		10 Roof mounted ventilation units.	
	11 Car parking ventilation: details to be stated.	nr		11 Car parking ventilation (i.e. air movement systems for removing fumes, smells and other contaminants of the air from car parks to the outside), including systems involving no air treatment and systems supplying fresh air to the car parking spaces.	
	12 Other local and special ventilation systems: details to be stated.	nr			

Sub-element	Component	Unit	Measurement rules for components	Included	Excluded
				12 Distribution ductwork and ductwork fittings and ancillaries, e.g. supports, hangers, access openings and dampers (control, fire and smoke). 13 Grilles, fans, filters and other ancillary components of central air conditioning systems. 14 Vibration isolation mountings. 15 Instrumentation and control components to local and special ventilation systems. 16 Sundry items. 17 Where works are to be carried out by a *subcontractor, subcontractor's preliminaries*, design fees, risk allowance, overheads and profit.	
3 Smoke extract/control **Definition:** Air movement and pressurisation systems for removing and controlling the build-up of smoke arising from a fire, and to assist in procuring the safety of personnel and in maintaining safe escape routes.	1 Smoke extract/control systems: details to be stated.	m²	C1 The area measured is the area serviced by the system (i.e. the area of the rooms and circulation spaces that are served by the system, which is not necessarily the total gross internal floor area (GIFA) of the building). The area serviced is measured using the rules of measurement for ascertaining the GIFA. C2 Where more than one system is employed, the area measured for each system is the area serviced by the system. Areas to be measured using the rules of measurement for ascertaining the GIFA. C3 Installations to residential units, hotel rooms, student accommodation units and the like may be enumerated (nr). The type of residential unit or room and size (by number of bedrooms) of unit is to be stated. C4 Work to existing buildings is to be described and identified separately.	1 Automatic smoke extract systems. 2 Automatic smoke compartmentalisation systems. 3 Fan units. 4 Distribution ductwork and ductwork fittings and ancillaries, e.g. supports, hangers, access openings and dampers (control, fire and smoke). 5 Grilles, fans, filters and other ancillary components of smoke ventilation systems. 6 Vibration isolation mountings. 7 Instrumentation and control components to smoke ventilation systems. 8 Sundry items. 9 Where works are to be carried out by a *subcontractor, subcontractor's preliminaries*, design fees, risk allowance, overheads and profit.	1 Roof vents and roof cowls (included in *sub-element* 2.3.5: Rooflights, skylights and openings). 2 General purpose low voltage (LV) power supplies (included in *sub-element* 5.8.2: Power installations). 3 Building management systems and other control systems (included in *sub-element* 5.12.3: Central control/building management systems (BMS)). 4 Builder's work in connection with services (included in element 5.14: Builder's work in connection with services). 5 Testing and commissioning of services (included in element 5.15: Testing and commissioning of services).

Element 5.8: Electrical installations

Sub-element	Component	Unit	Measurement rules for components	Included	Excluded
1 Electrical mains and sub-mains distribution: **Definition:** The distribution of LV electricity from (and including) the building main switchgear panel to (and including) the area distribution boards.	1 Electrical mains and sub-mains distribution: details to be stated.	m²	C1 The area measured is the total gross internal floor area (GIFA) of the building, measured using the rules of measurement for ascertaining the GIFA. C2 Installations to residential units, hotel rooms, student accommodation units and the like may be enumerated (nr). The type of residential unit or room and size (by number of bedrooms) of unit is to be stated) of unit is to be stated. C3 Work to existing buildings is to be described and identified separately.	1 Distribution of LV electricity from (and including) the building main switchgear panel to (and including) the area distribution boards. 2 HV switchgear. 3 LV switchgear and distribution boards. 4 HV and LV cables and wiring, including support components, cable trays and the like. 5 Conduits and cable trunking, including all fittings and support components. 6 Busbar trunking. 7 Earthing and bonding components. 8 Transformers. 9 Fuse pillars, base units, poles and accessories and the like. 10 Sundry items. 11 Where works are to be carried out by a *subcontractor, subcontractor's preliminaries*, design fees, risk allowance, overheads and profit.	1 Connections to statutory undertaker's electricity main (included in *sub-element* 8.7.2: Electricity mains supply). 2 Distribution of HV electricity to on-site transformer (included in *sub-element* 8.7.2: Electricity mains supply). 3 Transformer sub-stations, including packaged sub-stations main (included in *sub-element* 8.7.2 Electricity mains supply). 4 Distribution of LV electricity to main switchgear panel within the building, including main switchgear panel, cables, excavating and backfilling trenches and the like (included in *sub-element* 5.8.2: Power installations). 5 Electric generation installations within the building (included in *sub-element* 5.8.5: Local electricity generation systems). 6 Building management systems and other control systems (included in *sub-element* 5.12.3: Central control/building management systems (BMS)). 7 Builder's work in connection with services (included in *element* 5.14: Builder's work in connection with services). 8 Testing and commissioning of services (included in *element* 5.15: Testing and commissioning of services).

Sub-element	Component	Unit	Measurement rules for components	Included	Excluded
2 Power installations **Definition:** Sub-circuit power installations from sub-distribution boards terminating at socket outlets, fuse connection units and other accessories. Including final connections to permanent mechanical and electrical equipment.	1 Power installation: details to be stated.	m²	C1 The area measured is the area serviced by the system (i.e. the area of the rooms and circulation spaces that are served by the system, which is not necessarily the total gross internal floor area (GIFA) of the building). The area serviced is measured using the rules of measurement for ascertaining the GIFA. C2 Where more than one system is employed, the area measured for each system is the area serviced by the system. Areas to be measured using the rules of measurement for ascertaining the GIFA. C3 Installations to residential units, hotel rooms, student accommodation units and the like may be enumerated (nr). The type of residential unit or room and size (by number of bedrooms) of unit is to be stated. C4 Work to existing buildings is to be described and identified separately.	1 General low voltage (LV) power installations. 2 Extra LV supply installations. 3 Direct current (DC) installations. 4 LV switchgear and distribution boards, where not included as part of the sub-mains distribution. 5 Uninterruptible power supply (UPS) installations and the like. 6 Cables and wiring, including support components from sub-distribution boards to socket outlets, fuse connection units and the like. 7 Conduits and cable trunking, including all fittings and support components. 8 Earthing and bonding components. 9 Socket outlets, fuse connection units and other outlet accessories. 10 Final connections to equipment (e.g. boilers, kitchen and catering equipment, instantaneous water heaters, cookers and extract terminals). 11 Separate power installations to specialist mechanical and electrical equipment (e.g. to transportation systems). 12 Final connections to specialist mechanical and electrical equipment where not carried out by the equipment installer. 13 Sundry items. 14 Where works are to be carried out by a subcontractor, subcontractor's preliminaries, design fees, risk allowance, overheads and profit.	1 Electric heating installation (included in sub-element 5.6.1: Central heating or sub-element 5.6.2: Local heating, as appropriate). 2 LV switchgear and distribution boards, included as part of the sub-mains distribution (included in sub-element 5.8.1: Electrical mains and sub-mains distribution). 3 Final connections to specialist mechanical and electrical equipment where carried out by the equipment installer. 4 Building management systems and other control systems (included in sub-element 5.12.3: Central control/building management systems (BMS)). 5 Builder's work in connection with services (included in element 5.14: Builder's work in connection with services). 6 Testing and commissioning of services (included in element 5.15: Testing and commissioning of services).